Our Quaking Earth

By Elliott Roberts

DEEP SEA, HIGH MOUNTAIN

OUR QUAKING EARTH

Our Quaking Earth

by ELLIOTT ROBERTS

It is disturbing and terrifying to feel the supposedly solid and immovable earth moving back and forth. It is an eerie fantastic thing. We depend on the earth. If it won't stand still, what will then?

LITTLE, BROWN AND COMPANY
Boston · Toronto

LIBRARY OF CONGRESS CATALOG CARD NO. 63-14238

Fifth Printing

*Published simultaneously in Canada
by Little, Brown & Company (Canada) Limited*

PRINTED IN THE UNITED STATES OF AMERICA

Foreword

Elliott Roberts, for several years the administrative chief of the Division of Geophysics, Coast and Geodetic Survey, has always taken a deep interest in the earthquake investigations of the Division. An engineer by training, he worked long and hard to advance this work, particularly in the field of engineering seismology, which is concerned with the safety of structures. His extensive reading in the subject of earthquakes, earthquake history, and current earthquake research, and his never-failing eagerness to discuss the technical problems confronting the Division members, led him eventually to a broad semitechnical knowledge of the field.

This book is a result of his long interest. It is authoritative but not burdened with technicalities, and the wealth of anecdote and general commentary make it more interesting for the casual reader or scientific beginner than any textbook I know. As a professional seismologist, I express the hope that many young readers will find through this book that seismology is a field so interesting that they will wish to delve more deeply into it — perhaps to consider making it a life career.

DEAN S. CARDER
Research Seismologist
                    U. S. Coast and Geodetic Survey

Contents

To my wife, and to my young friends
who may learn from this book something
of the earth and what makes it quake.

Our Quaking Earth

Introduction —
The Sunken City

At seventeen minutes before noon on the seventh of June, 1692, two hundred years after Columbus discovered America, an era ended at Port Royal on the Caribbean island of Jamaica.

Port Royal, the center of English commercial activity in the New World, was a drab town spread treeless and glaring on a sandy spit near where Kingston now lies. But Jamaica itself was not drab. It lay north of Port Royal, presenting a skyline of jagged blue mountains shimmering in the sun. Its landscape was so rugged and broken that Columbus is said to have described it to his patroness Queen Isabella by crumpling a piece of paper to make a picture of it. Palms and brilliant flowers were everywhere. Peaceful indeed it seemed.

But Jamaica was not always peaceful. It was a

land of violence — smoldering always, blazing out all too often. The men of Port Royal called it "The Land of Look Behind" because of the danger of ambush besetting the traveler in its hills. It is known to scientists today as a land broken and up-ended by countless earthquakes in the long years of the earth's growth. Jamaica's beauty covered and hid much evil!

Port Royal, young America's busiest port, had many well-stocked warehouses and stores with prosperous merchants, some of whom may not have cared too much where their suppliers got their goods. It was the hangout of some of the roughest, most drunken sailors ever to be seen in one place on earth. It was also home port for many pirates of the Spanish Main — men like the cutthroat Henry Morgan, who sailed from Port Royal to loot Spanish treasure ships and to sack New World towns like Panama City. In 1692 Henry Morgan was already four years dead, buried beneath the sands of Port Royal Spit, but the town, despite a growing reformist movement, was still the scene of debauchery on a scale beyond belief. In the years of its existence on that tongue of land, Port Royal had earned the title "Wickedest City in the World." It was time for something to happen!

Among the better element who were trying to

make a decent town of Port Royal was the Reverend Emanuel Heath, rector of St. Paul's Church. Writing shortly after that fateful June seventh, he related that he and John White, the acting governor of Jamaica, had been about to take a glass of wormwood wine, just before noon that day, when the earth rolled and heaved up underfoot. He had never known such a thing.

"Lord, sir, what is this!" he cried.

Mr. White was reassuring. It was just an earthquake — soon to be over — the rector must not fear.

But the rector did fear, and well he might! The whole town was shaking. The ground rose and fell in waves like those of the sea. As he wrote later to a friend, it cracked open, and closed again, swallowing people and squeezing them to death. There was a great roaring, like mountains falling, as the whole north part of town slowly slid and fell into the sea. Thames Street, along the waterfront, and the heavy masonry walls of Fort James and Fort Carlisle all fell forever beneath the waters of the harbor. The descent, despite the earthquake's violence, was slow and ordered after a fashion, whole buildings settling majestically to a submerged rest where they can be seen through the water, almost intact, even today.

In the three separate shocks of the Port Royal

earthquake, numerous sloops and ships were lost in the wild waves and turbulence of the sea, two thousand of Port Royal's people disappeared, and no less than two thirds of the city itself was destroyed. Reverend Mr. Heath and Acting Governor White escaped death, but many of the waterfront bums and desperadoes who had been responsible for Port Royal's unique and infamous distinction died helplessly in the uproar. This marked the real end of Port Royal's dissipation, for the later reconstructed city was a much improved place.

Some think there is a lesson in this one of Nature's dramas. Jamaica, land of voodoo and black magic, lies quiet under its tropical sun, but simple people have wondered in the years since the Port Royal disaster if it was divine punishment that day in 1692. It seems to them right that an angry Providence would wipe out the inquity of a wicked city by sinking it in the sea.

Scientists, studying the history of geological change in the Caribbean earthquake belt, know the upheaval that ended the era of buccaneers at Port Royal to be a routine movement in a long process of earth adjustment. It just happened there at that time, but men will still ask why — and how it came to pass.

There is a long story behind our understanding

of these freaks of Nature. It begins with the awed wonder of primitive peoples, and leads onward through periods of superstition and religious mysticism to our modern era. It tells what we now know of events scores or hundreds of miles inside our earth.

I

Stories of Some Famous Earthquakes

The whole concord of the world consists in discord.
— SENECA

History is full of the stories of great earthquakes. Some are worth the telling, not to grieve over the suffering they caused, but because of their strange effects. Come with me into the past.

The first great earthquake of the Christian era, and among the earliest known to us, destroyed the city of Hsien, China. A.D. 7. Its early place in history is its only good reason for fame, for we know very little about it. A very strong quake hit Calcutta, India, on October 11, 1737, causing the dreadful toll of three hundred thousand deaths — more than the entire modern population of Miami, Florida, or the state of Nevada. Information about this frightful earthquake is also meager. We know much more of the great shock that destroyed Lisbon, Portugal, a few years later. It is one of the most famous in history. Some say it must have been the most spectacular, though it was less terrible in human losses than the Calcutta disaster.

And the sea leaped up

It was All Saints' Day, the first of November, 1755, at the time of the first Mass, and many of Lisbon's 235,000 people were at church. The city's houses lay clustered, rank on rank, over the low hills along the north bank of the River Tagus, six miles up from the sea. There were twenty thousand of them, four and five stories tall, that had stood more years than most people could remember. They seemed timeless and permanent.

Then suddenly it happened!

Deep in the earth not many miles southwest of Lisbon some kind of tremendous force was unleashed, and Lisbon's quiet was over. In the streets and houses and churches the people were surprised by quick, sharp vibrations that seemed to rattle their very bones. After a minute the vibrations came slower and much stronger. A roar like thunder deafened the ears and suffocating clouds of dust appeared over the city as the familiar old houses and churches began crumbling and falling to the ground. In another minute the motion of the ground changed to a violent up-and-down whiplashing that finished off most of the buildings that still stood. This was only the first of three great earthquakes that hit Lisbon that day.

As the roar from the churning ground and the crashing of falling buildings lessened, screams of trapped people could be heard everywhere. Then tongues of flame began to lick at curtains and wood-work that had fallen into the cooking fires and altar candles. Soon, fanned by a high wind, these grew into a vast fire that was to feed on the rubble for many days. There were few able men left to fight it, and in any case there was no water, and the nar-row streets were impassably choked with the rubble of thirty-two churches, fifty-three palaces, and thou-sands of lesser buildings. Even the public squares could not be recognized. As a city Lisbon was all but gone, with perhaps only three thousand cracked and dismal houses left standing on the hills farthest from the river. Then began the second earthquake!

It struck twenty minutes after the first. By now there wasn't much masonry left to fall, but this shock brought another kind of tragedy. Many sur-vivors had managed to crawl to the inviting firm-

ness of a new stone quay, the Cays Depreda on
the river front. Low and heavy, how could it fall?
But fall it did! In the renewed shaking of the city
its foundations gave way, and it sank forever into
the river with all its screaming people, just as the
Port Royal waterfront had done sixty-three years
before. None was ever found.

At about this time a slower effect of the first
earthquake added still another kind of terror. The
sea rose up to overwhelm the coast of Portugal in
a wave that was to spread in time throughout the
whole Atlantic. At the mouth of the Tagus River
there was a fall of the water that laid bare the
whole entrance bar, then on came a twenty-foot
foaming crest with force enough to go half a mile
inland over the rubble. Bridges were broken, walls
uprooted, and ships were torn loose and overturned
until the river became a tangle of masts and spars.

The effects in other places were astonishing. At
Colares, near Lisbon, the land rose permanently to
let people walk where water had always been, and
a rock never before seen by sailors rose out of the
waters of the harbor. Great areas of land along
the coast of Portugal came to rest at new levels.
The shock was felt throughout Portugal and Spain,
over an area of a million square miles. It is said
that extremely sensitive persons felt it at Venice,

nearly fifteen hundred miles northeastward, but we may safely doubt this.

Sloshing wave motions occurred in lakes as far away as Sweden. Scotland's storied Loch Lomond sloshed with a two-foot wave, and boats were torn loose from their moorings in the canals of Amsterdam. Well waters rose up. Springs were disturbed — some stopped flowing, and some gushed red water. The warm springs at Toplitz in Bohemia threw out mud. The sea wave generated in the Atlantic reached the coast of Britain by midafternoon, and the West Indies by early evening.

So-called companion shocks at almost the same instant did heavy damage in North Africa, many hundreds of miles away, but these must have been separate earthquakes. Scientists cannot say whether they were sympathetic earthquakes, triggered by the Lisbon shocks, or entirely different ones that just happened at that time.

The Lisbon earthquake left probably fifty thousand dead. Many, it is sad to say, died in the churches and chapels. The tragedy thus left for later generations some of the strongest impressions of this kind in all history. It even achieved a place in literature, for Voltaire wrote a *Poem on the Disaster of Lisbon* (1756), and he referred to it repeatedly in his beautifully written tale *Candide* (1759).

And the land fell

Quite different in many ways was the earthquake near New Madrid, Missouri, on December 16, 1811, the first of a long series of major shocks lasting until March of the following year. It was the strongest known to have occurred in the United States. But it was also remarkable in other ways. Its violence and effects were very unusual in the lowland reaches of a great valley, alongside such a river as the Mississippi. Many of its effects were in fact unmatched anywhere. But it killed almost no one, and its permanent results are obvious only to experts. Truly it was a scientist's earthquake.

It was in thinly settled country where most of the houses were log cabins. New Madrid itself was a village of fewer than a thousand persons. The evening of December 15 was clear and still, and nothing unusual was evident. The farmers and trappers could not know of the underground forces then getting ready to shake the valley land.

Soon after two o'clock in the morning there sounded a distant rumbling, then the houses groaned and swayed and their chimneys fell. The sky was darkened by the rising dust. Many persons reported flashes of lightning. All the houses of New Madrid were destroyed or nearly so, but farther out in the country few fell, for log cabins are well suited for shaking. Lesser aftershocks continued until soon after daylight, when another quake struck with all the violence of the first.

Many persons witnessed the almost unbelievable disturbances in the ground. J. Bradbury, an English botanist, was nearby. The naturalist Audubon, riding his horse in the nearby state of Kentucky, saw long waves rippling the surface of the land, like those of the sea. Captain Nicholas Roosevelt, navigating the first steamer to use the Mississippi, encountered heavy waves that overwhelmed many lesser boats. Major Long's exploration expedition was passing enroute to the far West, and his men were appalled at what they saw. From all these we have observations made with scientific care and thoroughness.

The wave motions in the ground tilted trees until their branches interlocked. Quicksand sinks pockmarked the land, and there were blowholes where spouting water had built sand hills a hundred feet across. Deep cracks appeared, and the earth slid down from the bluffs and low hills. Whole islands disappeared in the river, and channels were completely changed.

The most important and lasting effect was the change in level of thousands of square miles of the land — changes as much as ten or fifteen feet.

Tree stumps 150 years old in the drowned area of Reelfoot Lake, Tennessee, where the ground sank in the New Madrid earthquake of 1811.

Twenty square miles of sunken land in Tennessee soon filled with water, forming Reelfoot Lake, which is now an important wildlife refuge. More than two hundred square miles of forest were drowned, and even today after 150 years, thousands of stumps still protrude like ghosts from shallow water areas.

As in most great earthquakes, the ground disturbances were widely felt. In this the New Madrid earthquake matched the earlier performance at Lisbon, producing ground motions felt throughout a million square miles, even in places as far distant as Boston, more than a thousand miles away. Pendulum clocks were stopped throughout the eastern part of the country. People were badly frightened at Washington. Charleston, South Carolina, was so shaken that the bell rang in the spire of St. Philip's Church, just seventy-five years before Charleston suffered a great and historic earthquake of its own.

So many earthquakes followed that Dr. Robertson, of Sainte Genevieve, grew tired of counting them and stopped at five hundred. Jared Brooks of Louisville had more persistence, counting 1874 aftershocks between December 16 and March 15. Early in the series Brooks constructed pendulums of different lengths and spring devices of great ingenuity, intended to detect vibrations not otherwise likely to be noticed. He thus became one of America's earliest instrumental earthquake observers — an activity now highly developed by use of instruments of exquisite sensitivity. Dwindling shocks went on for more than a year, but the people became indifferent and stopped paying attention.

Perhaps the most violent

This earthquake, for all its tremendous effects and its record as America's greatest, was not the greatest known to the world. The Assam earthquake of June 12, 1897, was much stronger.

Just as at New Madrid, changes of ground level occurred over large areas. It was in fact a violent incident in the upward growth of the four-thousand-foot Assam Hills, south of India's Brahmaputra

River, whose summits are elevated remnants of the ancient plain of Sylhet. Surveyors found the uplift in this shock alone to be some twenty feet. There was complete destruction, reported as "terrible," throughout nine thousand square miles, and the area where the vibrations were felt was twice that of the Lisbon and New Madrid shocks. One authority, Nicholas Heck, called it the "most violent of known history."

And the fires raged

The New Madrid earthquake, the strongest in our country's history, is known to very few people alive today, while a strong but much lesser shock that visited San Francisco in 1906 is familiar to practically all informed people. Doubtless it will occupy space in history books for generations to come. The difference is that between the shaking of some log cabins and the destruction of many square miles of a large city. What happened in San Francisco makes a dramatic story.

The California earthquake of April 18, 1906, was the third really great one to strike California in historic times. In 1857 Fort Tejon, near Los Angeles, had been terribly shaken. The hamlet of Lone Pine, in the Owens Valley east of the Sierras, had been destroyed in 1872. Those were great earth-

Street scene following the San Francisco earthquake and fire of 1906.

quakes, but the country was sparsely settled, and few suffered. Not so at San Francisco.

It was a few minutes after five o'clock in the morning. Most people were asleep, but the sounds of the milkmen and the early streetcars signified a large city awakening to another busy day. It was awakening to a kind of grief we can now hardly imagine!

At that moment the land moved in a shudder that knocked down buildings, including the new seven-million-dollar city hall the citizens were so proud of. It started fires from upset stoves and flashing electric wires, and broke all the water mains.

The rocks had broken apart along nearly three hundred miles of a well-known crack in the California land, a remarkable feature known as the San Andreas Fault, though some call it the "earthquake crack."

The center of the break was near San Francisco, and there the damage was greatest. Some seven hundred persons died under falling buildings and from diseases springing up in the unsanitary camps later occupied by the homeless people. The property loss was enormous. Fires, with no water to stop them, got out of control. Before they died out, four square miles of the city were blackened ruins. The fire loss itself was four hundred million dollars, more than nine-tenths of all the damage. This was a grievous amount in those days, although it might have been exceeded but for the daring of the city authorities, who used dynamite to remove hundreds of houses in the path of the spreading fire. This opened fire lanes to check the further spread of the flames, but it drew forth vigorous opposition from the property owners.

The effects of the earthquake were widespread. Springs stopped running and the ground water changed its flow patterns. Within a half mile of the breaking fault aged white oak trees six feet in diameter were uprooted. A wet meadowland area slid half a mile downhill, and the road between Point Reyes and Inverness, in Marin County, was broken apart and offset twenty-one feet where it crossed the fault. This great movement was long thought to be a world's record of horizontal shifting, though greater up-and-down movements have been known.

The California earthquake is remembered as one of the great tragedies of American history. It was unexpected and shocking to the country. Actually, its death toll is now exceeded almost any week on American highways, but we are so used to automobile accidents that we pay them little attention. Earthquakes are more dramatic!

San Francisco is also remembered by scientists for the investigations that resulted. The causes and effects were studied by teams of American and Japanese engineers. The rebuilt city of San Francisco now contains many features intended to strengthen the buildings and to provide an almost unfailing water supply in case of another such earthquake. The water mains are in duplicate, with many con-

trol valves to permit sending water by different routes
around broken places. There are also large underground reservoirs for emergency use. The people
have done everything possible to prevent and control fires, which, as we have seen, are sometimes
worse than the earthquakes themselves.

Study of the split rocks along the San Andreas
Fault brought forth much new knowledge. It helped
to confirm American ideas about the sources of
earthquakes. Having the major effects of the break
visible on the surface of the ground meant that
scientists were able to see much of what actually
happened to the land. This helped settle disputes
among earthquake specialists about the true reasons
for such earth spasms.

A nation stunned

The first earthquake of sufficient consequence to
become a national tragedy wrecked Tokyo and
Yokohama, in the growing nation of Japan, on Sep-
tember 1, 1923. It has been named the Kwanto
earthquake after the province nearest where it
started.

Office workers were spilling out of the downtown
buildings, seeking luncheon seats in the restaurants
or on the grassy spaces of the city parks. A priest

was stepping toward the platform where he would toll the noontime bells. It was a peaceful, sunny fall day, and the air everywhere was languid.

It seemed that Nature must have been impatient with all this peacefulness. At one and a half minutes before noon the first gentle release of energy began under the waters of Sagami Bay. The gentleness didn't last long. The disturbance quickly migrated forty miles northward toward Japan's two great cities. On arrival it delivered a punch that meant catastrophe and a huge toll of life and property.

Trains lurched wildly on the Tokyo-Yokohama interurban line, then ground to a halt, balked by twisted rails and landslides. The priest jumped to escape the falling bells. The great Imamura, one of the foremost earthquake scientists, sat in his Tokyo office, professionally timing the ground shocks. He rapidly became alarmed at their growing severity. Finally, with bedlam everywhere, he rose to look over the city. Where it had stood in peace a few moments before, it was now a gruesome shambles, horrible to see.

In Yokohama eleven thousand buildings collapsed and nearly fifty-nine thousand burned. In Tokyo more than a third of a million buildings were burned by fires driven by high winds. Bridges were thrown down, forests and cultivated fields ruined, and railroad tunnels were closed. Raging waves in Sagami Bay deluged the shores at heights reported to be thirty-five feet, adding to the destruction, loss of life, and suffering. In the entire area nearly one hundred thousand died, and more than that were injured. A million people became homeless.

The total loss has been estimated to be nearly three billion dollars, not to mention two-thousand-year-old art treasures and irreplaceable national records. Even the great bronze Buddha at Kamakura moved sidewise on his pedestal. Some faithful persons may have taken this as a sign of divine displeasure.

Japanese losses were not entirely unforeseen. Imamura himself had predicted nearly twenty years before that Tokyo would have a great earthquake. He even warned that one hundred thousand might die if the water system and fire-fighting equipment were not improved. The losses, grimly predicted by Imamura in his wisdom, were largely due to the widespread use of flimsy and inflammable building materials. This has been traditional Japanese practice because of economic circumstances and the easy availability of bamboo and other light materials.

The Japanese engineers are well aware of the dangers of these methods, and have worked diligently to improve building methods, particularly for large business and industrial structures. Many large buildings of moderate height withstood the shock of the Kwanto earthquake very well, and certainly many of those erected in the later reconstruction are as safe as human ingenuity can make them. The new Tokyo also featured wider streets and many parks and refuge areas.

Hydrographic surveys of Sagami Bay, where this convulsion began, seemed to show changes of unbelievable magnitude. It was reported that five hundred square miles of the bay bottom changed shape, some areas rising or subsiding hundreds of feet. It has been suggested that these submarine changes were from large-scale slumping of soft materials, perhaps ashes from old eruptions of the famous and beautiful volcano Fujiyama. But this seems impossible, and it raises questions about the accuracy of the old surveys used for comparison. However, it is certain that large changes did occur, confirming our ideas that great earthquakes signify an always restless earth.

The sea bottom changes in Sagami Bay, whatever their size, furnished a clue to the nature of the sea waves that often follow strong undersea shocks. It happened here and at Lisbon, and elsewhere. Even the waters of the sea, fluid and adaptable as they are, are shocked into destructive action when the shape of their bed is changed so suddenly.

Despite the grim events of the time, the Japanese people remained stoic and did not panic. Government regulations designed to prevent profiteering turned out to be unnecessary. Public health was safeguarded by sanitary measures and inspections. Perhaps the most significant result of all was the flood of relief goods and supplies contributed by the nations of the world. It was a remarkable expression of good will and brotherly affection.

During two years and more, while the industrious Japanese painstakingly rebuilt their ruined cities, many hundreds of aftershocks of the Kwanto earthquake rocked the Japanese land. The people knew this was normal. Probably they told themselves that the remaining stresses in the ground were being released gently in this way, and as long as the shaking continued they had little more to fear. In time it was clear that the aftershocks were farther apart and ever weaker. An end was in sight. Finally, in November, 1925, the great Imamura pronounced everything back to normal. The pretty Japanese countryside was having only two shocks a day!

And the mountains rocked

On August 15, 1950, there was another calamity in the world. One of the most violent earthquakes of modern times drove the recordings wildly off the paper of most earthquake recorders everywhere. At Washington, Miss Crone of my office saw the recording pen go into violent swinging. She was probably the first person in the world outside the central earthquake area to know of Nature's newest convulsion. She called me in excitement, and our Government specialists went immediately to work analyzing the marks. Soon earthquake scientists everywhere were studying their confused recordings, trying to guess where the great shock had been. One guessed Alaska. Another thought it was in the South Pacific. Others chose South America or Japan. Radio announcers, reporting these wild guesses, made quite a story of this "greatest earthquake of the age," which no scientist could find. A lost earthquake, indeed! The joke soon ended. In four hours Leonard Murphy, of our office, known widely as "Mr. Earthquake," had announced the correct location. It was in the mountainous never-never land of Tibet, near the borders of China and India.

Here no international relief was needed. The stricken people were shy, half-savage mountain tribesmen and a few Indian border guardsmen. It took three years for some of their stories to filter out of the wilderness, and no one has any idea how many victims there were. No more than fourteen credible witnesses could be found in months of search.

The Himalayan earthquake of 1950 was one of the most violent since modern instruments have given means for comparison. It represented a step in the geologically rapid rise of the Himalayas, the highest mountains on earth. Its energy has been estimated to match that of one hundred thousand atomic bombs of the type used at Hiroshima, Japan, in the last days of World War II.

Ten thousand square miles of land were churned into desolation. Changes in the landscape probably exceeded anything before known to scientists. The mountains, waterlogged by the monsoon rains, slumped down in thousands of landslides, so that the superintending engineer of Assam later estimated the total rock fall at more than two billion tons — enough to fill a hundred-car freight train every five minutes day and night for two years. An awful rumbling from the bowels of the earth grew into a deafening roar, and the sky was darkened by clouds of dust and driving sand. Near the central area it was impossible for anyone to stand, and people seven hundred miles away at Calcutta were alarmed.

The stories of the few eyewitnesses sounded like nightmares. One Briton in the outer area of lesser intensity said it was "Hell minus ten degrees Fahrenheit." In a closer place members of a military patrol said they saw four men and a mule fall into a new twenty-foot chasm and end up submerged in a lake of sulphurous mud.

In the Brahmaputra Valley far south of the mountains the earth heaved and rolled so people became seasick. Cars rolled a half mile. A nine-hundred-foot stretch of railway sank sixteen feet, and roads were cracked so they could not be used. But the worst was yet to come in the rich tea gardens of Assam.

Countless mountain streams, swollen by the monsoon rains, were dammed by landslides and their flow ceased entirely. But this was not for long. Within days the newly formed lakes filled so the water overtopped the loosely piled landslide materials that had checked their flow. Quickly the new dams were washed away in sudden floods that gushed down from the mountains to overwhelm thousands of square miles of the Brahmaputra Valley, washing away the tea plantations, forming vast swamps and morasses foul with dead fish and evil smells, and ruining agriculture for years.

The Andes keep on growing

In the shaky region of South America's west coast mountain ranges, there came the earthquakes of May 22, 1960, under the sea near Valdivia, Chile. The strongest of that swarm of strong earthquakes ranks among the greatest of the age. It destroyed Concepción for the sixth time in the city's four centuries of life. Valdivia, Puerto Montt, and other cities were wrecked. Sea waves raced over the Pacific. Old volcanoes, sprung to life, threw lava and ashes over the country. The ground shocks, volcanic eruptions, and landslides convulsed ninety thousand square miles, bringing ruin to an area greater than all of Great Britain. In the beautiful lake country mountains crumbled and a twenty-five-mile stretch of high mountain land slid down a thousand feet. On the coast people ran to higher ground in fear of sea waves only to be swept back into the sea by landslides. Fifty thousand homes were destroyed. A quarter of Chile's seven million people suffered cold and hunger, for communications, water supplies, sanitary facilities, and power were all lost. The violence of this tremendous shock was so great that the entire earth was still pulsating with its vibrations after several days.

People of the present age may protect themselves

through the knowledge gained by our growing earthquake science. In southern Chile scientists and engineers are now planning reconstruction works that should mean Concepción and the other cities will suffer less in the future.

II

Earthquakes, Superstition, and Fear

First get your facts, and then you can distort them at your leisure.

— MARK TWAIN

One time in 1946, four of us — three from the Coast and Geodetic Survey and one from Fordham University — found ourselves on the West Indies island of Hispaniola. A strong shock had damaged Santiago and other northern towns of the Dominican Republic. The disturbance had come from under the sea near the five-and-one-half-mile abyss called the Brownson Deep, driving up sea waves to add to the damage.

We were there at the invitation — I almost said "command" — of dictator Rafael Trujillo, who ruled the country's life and affairs. Concerned by the confusion after the earthquake, he had determined to reassure and quiet the people. Many had quit work to pray and wail. Others, seeking to placate God, whom they believed to be angry, paraded about with stones and ashes on their heads, *penitentes* atoning for their sins.

Wanting the people back at work, Trujillo had asked our group to review the quake and determine whether the worst was over. He had the newspapers print big headlines about our "North American Scientific Mission," and he expected us to make public speeches of reassurance. As it turned out, we could do so. It seemed all over but for the usual long string of lessening aftershocks. Having viewed the damage and put modern instruments in an observatory to keep track of things, we made the speeches. People went back to work. Trujillo had had his way, as usual.

We have already read of people who believed the Port Royal earthquake to be a divine punishment for human sins. It may be hard to believe that in this scientific twentieth century there are still countries not a thousand miles from the United States where the people are so fearful of earthquakes that they must chastise themselves in atonement! By what means do they think God produces that powerful shaking of the ground?

Looking backward, we find such notions arising

out of fantastically wild imaginings about our earth
and what happens to it. Natural events were great
mysteries to our remote ancestors.

Snakes, frogs and other beasts

One of the commonest of human experiences is
gravity. Even the simplest beings know that things
fall unless supported. It is a fact of life — like fire
being hot and water being wet. So we find men from
the dawn of history wondering what supports the
earth itself. This basic and natural problem appealed
to the human mind. Ever curious, and reaching beyond his own capacity to understand, early man
dreamed up a world of mystery and magic.

We must thank L. Don Leet of Harvard University for a number of the ideas I shall relate from
his book *Causes of Catastrophe*. Some of the tales
describe the imaginings of simple people; others
were invented long ago by crafty individuals who
sought to become known as men of superior knowledge or magical powers. Unfortunately such men
still prowl our world.

One Burmese tribe had the tradition that the
earth was girdled by serpents. Occasionally one
would mistake his own tail for food. In the commotion of trying to catch it, he would cause the
whole earth to tremble. In the Moluccas the natives

*Some ancient Asians believed a frog supported the earth;
when he tired and moved a foot he shook things and made an
earthquake. Of course those people had no idea how big the
earth is, nor that it is really a ball as we know it to be.*

also believed in snakes. The Hindus told of a whole
series of serpents holding up the earth to keep it
from sinking in the sea. Passing the burden from
one to another, they would sometimes shake everything, causing an earthquake.

There were endless variations of these themes,
generally involving animals. They were important
figures in ancient times, for they did work for man.
The larger ones were admired for their strength, and
clearly should have been assigned the most important
tasks. In the East Indies it was the water buffalo
that supported the earth. In the Celebes it was the
hog, which shook the earth when he scratched himself against a palm tree. The Mongolian lamas, or

priests, preached that the Deity had put the earth in the care of a monster frog invented for the purpose. Whenever he moved part of his body the earth region nearest that part was shaken.

Some East African tribes, with even more imagination, told of a fish in the sea, carrying a stone on its back on which there stood a cow. At the top of this unusual heap, stuck on her horn, the cow carried the earth. Naturally she became tired from time to time and had to change horns. The shock of this was an earthquake!

Such notions were widespread, even among the ancient Greeks and Romans, who developed advanced civilizations ahead of most of the rest of the world. Gradually men came to realize the absurdity of these ideas about monster animals no one had ever seen. It became necessary to invent fantastic beings, which were thought to be more probable.

Special gods and giants were common in early times. The Greeks had their Atlas, so strong that he held the earth on his shoulders. He was not blamed for the frequent Greek earthquakes. Since they were thought to be most common near the coast, the sea god Poseidon, like his Roman counterpart Neptune, was supposed to have charge of earthquakes. He was in fact known also as "Earthshaker."

A Rumanian legend of singular beauty told how the earth rested on three half-divine pillars named Faith, Hope, and Charity. With a charming touch of religious feeling, the legend explained that when one of these symbols of morality wavered through the misdeeds of the people, the earth shook.

Many of the great philosophers of old considered the problem of earthquakes, as we know through the writings of Seneca, Pliny, Aristotle, and others. The Roman poet Ovid wrote that when the sun in its wanderings came too close, the earth, as a living and sensitive being, trembled in trying to shield itself from burning under the heat. This thought is not so remote, after all, from the idea of many present-day people that hot weather causes explosions in the earth!

It was commonly believed that foreign matter entered the earth, causing too much pressure. The resulting disturbances of the crowded materials were felt by humans as earthquakes. Anaxagoras, a Greek of the fifth century B.C., believed in a mysterious ether, perhaps related to our atmosphere, which he thought entered the earth with the rainfall. Democritus, who lived at the same time, imagined it to be the rain water itself, or seepage from lakes and the sea, which caused the trouble. In any event, here is the germ of another idea that won't die, for

some still think rainfall creates earthquake conditions.

Aristotle and the classicists

Aristotle, who lived in Greece in the fourth century before Christ, earned one of the most famous
names of all. He applied his superb intellect to the
explanation of nearly all things on earth. Unfortunately he lived long before the birth of the *scientific
method,* which today governs our efforts to understand Nature.

In modern science, ideas grow out of the clear observations of objective watchers. Observers seek
truth itself — not merely support for some pre-fixed
ideas. By combining unquestioned facts, and apply-
ing careful logic and deduction, the scientist builds
his laws. If there is any guessing or speculation involved, the results are looked on as *hypotheses,* or
simply working theories which are subject to correc-
tion.

It is strange that men of the great mental powers
of the classical philosophers failed to adopt the
simple notion of scientific objectivity — of believing
only what was obvious under observation and logic.
But their habits of thought led them into different
ways.

Having no technique for investigation or experiment, their imaginations had to come into play to invent, rather than to discover, reasons for everything. This invests the views of the day regarding natural phenomena with a certain air of unreality in the eyes of moderns. And this is all the more so because of a preoccupation in their time with flowery language, as if to improve the beauty of their ideas.

After long discussion of the writings of Democritus and other philosophers, Aristotle produced his own explanations of earthquakes in fantastic detail and variety. He spoke of the earth as trembling like a feverish man. It was made of the four elements then recognized. They were fire, air, water, and earth. With these he combined human experiences of hurricanes, volcanoes, and earthquakes. Out of his lengthy treatment there emerged a basic and not very new theme involving the escape of air imprisoned in caverns below the ground.

This idea has appeared in many forms and places. Seneca of Rome asked in the first century, "Can any one doubt that There and Therasia, four centuries before Christ, and this island which in our days and under our very eyes rose out of the Aegean Sea, were carried up to the light by the force of air?"

Aristotle also said that earthquakes were more numerous during moon eclipses and in the midst of tempests, neither of which is true. The fallacy of "earthquake weather," which apparently will not die, is most certainly a legacy from the inventive mind of the great Aristotle. And there is more — seemingly an endless store of it.

It was nearly two thousand years later when Shakespeare, writing his play *Henry IV,* presented a vivid picture of the London earthquake of 1580. Likening the earth to a human being, the character Glendower tells us, "The frame and huge foundation of the earth shak'd like a coward . . . the earth did tremble." In Macbeth we read, "Some say the earth was feverish and did shake."

The English writer Thomas Twyne, who witnessed the same London earthquake, has given us a more detailed account of it. Twyne observed keenly and accurately, though his descriptions seem quaint today. He presented a surprising amount of genuine information under a title which I cannot resist repeating: "A shorte and pithie discourse concerning the engendring, tokens, and effects of all Earthquakes in Generall: Particularly applyed and conferred with that most strange and terrible worke of the Lord in shaking the Earth, not only within the Citie of London, but also in most parts of all Englande: Which hapned vpon Wensday in Easter weeke last past, which was the sixt day of April, almost at sixe a clocke in the euening, in the yeare of our Lord GOD 1580."

In Twyne's pamphlet we learn that "Some imputed the ratling of wainescotes to Rattes and Weesels: the shaking of the beddes, tables and stooles, to Dogges . . . the very shakinge caused the Belles in some Steeples to knoll a stroake or twaine . . ." Quite evident was Twyne's uncertainty between the traditional views of Aristotle and the growing philosophy of Divine control. God was believed by the modernists to control all events for the achievement of His purposes. This being the case, the reasons and mechanism of natural phenomena were not understandable by men.

We should not hold it against Shakespeare, the playwright, and the intelligent Twyne, that they subscribed to fanciful ideas about earthquakes. They were not naturalists, and they lived in a world still steeped in superstition.

The long era of religious dogma

Strong religious preoccupations of people since Biblical times have quite naturally colored their ideas of the world we inhabit. In Italy in the early Christian era, it was believed that the Jew Malco, who struck Christ as he climbed Calvary, was punished by being sentenced to turn the post supporting the earth. He was supposed to have struck the post from time to time, hoping the earth would crumble and relieve him of his endless task.

The sixth-century Byzantine emperor Justinian decreed the death penalty for a series of offenses, including blasphemy and swearing by the hair of one's head, on the grounds that such practices were known to provoke thunderbolts and earthquakes. The modern writer A. H. Campbell has declared that this was clearly an excellent reason — as long as Justinian believed in its truth! I think we must agree.

Later religious interest in earthquakes took somewhat less fantastic turns but continued to be far more emotional than sensible. In 1661 Thomas Burnet foretold the end of the world in Latin, the classical language of scholarship. He said the present earth, an unsatisfactory successor to the one more or less destroyed by the Biblical flood, would some time be destroyed by earthquakes and fire. It would naturally begin at Rome, the seat of the kind of religious thinking he disapproved. England would be particularly unpleasant because of the coal fields, which would burn very hotly!

In Europe in the later 1700's frightened people crowded the churches after earthquake shocks, easy audiences for gloomy sermons about the need for penitence, and better behavior and morals. In 1777 the great church leader John Wesley wrote, "There is no Divine visitation which is likely to have so general an influence upon survivors as an earthquake."

An early New England preacher proclaimed that earthquakes were signs of the "chastening [purifying] rod of God." He was satisfied to "prove" this by asserting that earthquakes struck only cities, where people were — "not bare cliffs nor uninhabited beaches." Like Aristotle, it concerned him not at all that this belief was completely untrue. It would never have occurred to him to inquire into the question of its truth.

The false idea that earthquakes visited only populated places persisted long. This was doubtless a result of the scarcity of people in isolated places, and of the lack of instruments capable of indicating the actual locations of remote shocks. No less an authority than the British Royal Society published a statement in its *Transactions* of 1752, saying that earthquakes occurred only where people needed chastening! This kind of wrong reasoning reminds me of the story of the experimenter who trained fleas to jump at his command, but found that they refused to answer his command after he had pulled off their legs. He therefore wrote in his notebook that fleas became deaf when their legs were removed!

As we shall see, earthquakes occur in all sorts of places, although it must be admitted that people pay more attention to those which shake down their houses and dry up their drinking wells.

Some practical-minded preachers, feeling the need of more convincing explanations, kept alive the views of the long-dead Aristotle. In 1727 the Reverend John Barnard, of Marblehead, explained that practical people must in all common sense believe in caverns or hollows in the earth, which contain wind or water disturbed by underground fires. The resulting earthquakes must be expected to throw out venomous fumes causing vile diseases. This, of course could happen only under the will of God, who thus displayed His wrath. This theme, with its air of realism, certainly impressed and probably also scared the people squirming in John Barnard's hard pews.

Science in amateur hands

In the late 1600's religious belief had already achieved a queer sort of "scientific" flavor. Joseph Addison, the English writer, told in *The Tatler* of an impudent scoundrel who sold pills claimed to be "very good against earthquakes." Supernatural control of world events was widely discussed and much believed — such things, for instance, as an avenging angel who struck the air to make it vibrate and jar the earth as a lesson to erring humans.

In the middle of the eighteenth century the settlers in the New England colonies became disturbed over the suggestion that the "electrical substance" drawn from the air by Mr. Franklin's newfangled lightning rods might be responsible for earthquakes, particularly in cities like Boston, having "many points of iron sticking up."

Of course this kind of false reasoning is no new thing. It has gone on since even before Aristotle. And it goes on today. Uninformed persons habitually associate all sorts of unrelated ideas and discoveries in natural science. Who hasn't heard people complain that the firing of atomic bombs must be the cause of heavy rains — or dry spells, or even their aching corns! Some people fret because scientists won't listen when they explain that tropical hurricanes or volcanic eruptions could be stopped by the use of such bombs. Still others "discover" that magnetic forces have bent the earth's gravity sidewise, or can make cars roll uphill in some places. The variety of such meaningless ideas is amazing.

The chastening effect of burning

The great eighteenth-century earthquake disaster at Lisbon focused attention on such events and stimulated thinking about their causes. The state of real scientific knowledge having advanced but little, imagination ran riot. Moralists and opportunists made capital of the event. People wrote cynically of the profit to be made by the heirs of the dead, and by the masons who would rebuild the city.

The great minds of the day also went to work on it. Voltaire wrote his *Poem on the Disaster at Lisbon* with a foreword rebuking the cynics and wiseacres. He also dwelt on the event at great length in his novel *Candide*. We find Candide's companion Pangloss explaining that the South American town of Lima had had an earthquake the year before. This being a similar thing, it was clear that there was a vein of sulphur under the earth from Lima to Lisbon!

Candide was written to oppose and ridicule the theory, then fashionable, that the world was the best of all worlds — that everything was for the best. To illustrate his attitude Voltaire wrote vivid and fanciful episodes. Candide and Pangloss, imprisoned as unbelievers after their arrival at Lisbon, finally became involved in an auto-da-fé, the ceremonious trial and execution of religious unbelievers. Such ceremonies were common in the time of the Spanish Inquisition.

In Voltaire's story, scholars of the University of

Coimbra had announced that the burning of a few unbelievers or sinners would be an excellent way of warding off future earthquakes. (This was well in the tradition of the Archbishop of Trier, who, a century and a half before, had burned 120 fellow Germans because they had unduly delayed the coming of better weather!)

The Lisbon authorities, Candide found, had therefore seized a Basque who had married his godmother, and two citizens who had betrayed their Jewish faith by refusing to eat the bacon from a larded chicken. These poor victims were burned publicly over a slow fire. Pangloss was hanged until half dead, and Candide was flogged. In this subtle way the authorities acted to forestall future earthquakes. Unfortunately, that same day there was another noisy and damaging earthquake. Thus Voltaire tried to show that everything was *not* for the best!

This imaginative fiction preceded by only a few years the actual auto-da-fé of 1761, a consequence of the earthquake. The Marques of Pombal, then Secretary of State, was the strong administrator who managed the rebuilding and restoration of Lisbon. He was a practical man with no patience for the calamity-howlers, religious fanatics, and opportunists who impeded the work at hand. He became hopelessly impatient with a very popular priest,

Malagrida. This man, formerly a favorite of the royal family, was now devoting himself aggressively to scaring the people into retreat for contemplation and prayer. This interfered with Pombal's plans. The priest was therefore turned over to the Inquisition, tried, sentenced, and burned in Rossio Square.

Pombal had been irked at the outset by the reluctance of people to help in the clean-up work. They thought they needn't hurry to dispose of the waste and remove the unsanitary conditions. A certain Dr. da Silva had proclaimed that there could be no danger of a plague, for most certainly plagues could start only in Africa! A year after the earthquake Pombal had been forced to arrest people who prophesied another shock on the anniversary date. They did this to frighten people away from their houses, leaving them unguarded and open to pillage and burglary.

The Lisbon affair caused bitter religious quarrels that lasted many years. The central issue was always whether earthquakes were "natural" events — simple accidents of nature — or instruments of God's wrath punishing mortal sins and immorality. Even the realists who insisted on the naturalist viewpoint always added hastily, "Of course God *could* use earthquakes as punishment if He wished." Perhaps they feared the Inquisition. Most people did in those days!

The most important reason why this quarreling never ended was simply that no one knew what caused earthquakes. Science had not progressed enough to give men the necessary understanding.

Complete understanding has not been gained even today. Scientists do not understand as well as they could wish, and ordinary people are often quite mystified by earthquakes.

What can one believe?

Among the effects most often reported by people who experience earthquakes are mysterious lights. They are described as flashes, pillars, beams or globes, soft lights, or even soft glowing in the clouds or in the earth itself. Often they are said to be seen in daylight. But of course so is ordinary lightning.

Electrical storms do sometimes happen during earthquakes, but reports of lights have often been made when there was no storm. After the New Madrid earthquake such reports were especially numerous. Some natives of the area believed that they were actual volcanic eruptions, although scientists will assure anyone that no eruptions can possibly have occurred in that vicinity for many millions of years, if indeed ever. One result of the New Madrid shock was the stirring up of great clouds of dust. These may generate lightning flashes almost as readily as rain clouds do.

The famous Montessus de Ballore, an early student of South American earthquakes, looked carefully into this question, and discovered persons who had seen sparks jumping from telegraph or electric lines during an earthquake.

In modern populated areas the great number of electric transmission lines makes it almost certain that outdoor observers *will* see flashes of light when there are shocks strong enough to disturb the wires. In any event, earthquakes do not directly produce lights, and we may make our own guesses as to what really is the cause.

It isn't quite the same with another popular idea — that of earthquake weather. Carlyle, in discussing the French Revolution, wrote, "Hope ushers in a revolution as earthquakes are preceded by bright weather." The only trouble with this is that it isn't true. Many believers in earthquake weather, indeed, say that it must be hot and humid. Others believe almost anything else you can think of. A Professor Conroy made much of the weather conditions preceding the Long Beach, California, shock of 1933, convincing no one. The Japanese scientist Omori studied eighteen major earthquakes in Japan, but failed to find any rule as far as weather was concerned. So we may reject the idea of earthquake weather. There is no known connection between weather and earthquakes.

The next in our series of popular earthquake myths is earth fissures. There have been many tales about cracks opening in the earth to swallow whole villages. We do know that people and objects have been lost in the cracking of the topsoil or in slumping ground. But we must remember that these are superficial effects — not true openings of the earth itself. In any case such things are very rare. The Japanese Imamura has written that there is no proven record of men or animals being swallowed in this way in the entire history of Japan. The idea has been grossly overworked.

The primitive tribesmen of Assam refused to discuss the great shock of 1950, when questioned afterward by scientists. They believed the old quip, "Talk of evil spirits and they will appear!" Modern civilized people, with perhaps a slight show of bravado, say with pride that they "live on the earthquake line." It must be quite a long line, it seems to me. After all, such an attitude is just as much a matter of superstition as an unreasonable fear would be — like the lady who said she wasn't superstitious because *she* thought the number thirteen was lucky!

III

How Earthquakes Really Happen

There is nothing permanent except change.
— HERACLITUS

The wild jungle-clad mountains of New Guinea, soaring two thousand feet higher than any peaks in California or Colorado, rose out of the sea not many geological ages ago. They are young — much younger than the European Alps.

People fortunate enough to visit the peak of Santo Tomas, standing seven thousand feet above the plains of central Luzon in the Philippines, may scratch in the hardened soil and pick out ancient seashells. Passengers on Panagra's airliners flying over the Andes between Chile and Argentina have a breathtaking view of Aconcagua, at nearly twenty-three thousand feet the highest point in the Western world. Aconcagua's rocky cliffs are streaked at crazy angles by uncounted layers of rock, formed ages ago by the settling of sand and lime in some forgotten sea.

The atolls of the western Pacific are coral reefs that have grown up from the shoulders of old sunken mountains. The coral-building polyps add little by little to keep level with the sea as the mountains sink farther below the waves. Things done "little by little" can become very great if there is enough time. At Eniwetok Atoll, where many of our bomb tests have been conducted, the limestone mass capping the volcanic foundation of the island has a volume of more than two hundred and fifty cubic miles. This would be enough to lay a superhighway pavement a mile wide and five feet thick from here to the moon! And practically every bit of that limestone was made by shallow-water animals! They had time to do it.

Almost a live thing — our earth

If the earth seems solid and unchanging, it is because we see so brief a portion of its life process going on. Geologists know that a speeded-up motion picture, if we could compress a million years into a few minutes, would show the earth always writhing and squirming. Continuous change would be everywhere. Even though we don't see it actually happening, the rocks tell the story.

Bare mountain cliffs and the banks of river gorges tell of rocks risen up to become the backbones of whole mountain ranges. They have ridden high, often being bent into the most distorted shapes imaginable. Sometimes the layers stand on end. Sometimes they are overturned and lie upside down!

Such changes have required almost countless millions of years in long spaces of time called geological eras. In all this time the oceans and the continents have been almost completely changed time and again. And the changes have not always been quiet and peaceful. They have been marked by fre-

Bare cliffs showing distorted rock strata.

Courtesy U. S. Geological Survey

quent breaking of the rock layers when they could not reshape themselves fast enough.

With growing pains

Our old earth breaks apart with a shudder when its outer layers become stretched or squeezed or twisted beyond the strength of the rocks. This is an earthquake.

Perhaps it is really a growing pain. The earth may be growing so as to stretch its outer layers and crack apart, or perhaps shrinking so as to wrinkle it, like a dried apple skin. No one knows whether either is really happening, but surely something is! To understand this it is well to know a little about our earth and the forces that bend and squeeze its crust. This is not too easy, since no part of the earth is as unknown and mysterious as the rocks more than a few thousand feet under our feet.

Every American schoolboy or girl knows that the earth is round like a ball, slightly flattened near the north and south poles, and bulging at the equator like a fat man. Before the age of exploration many men believed the earth to be flat like a plate. There are still a few people here and there who think so, but they cannot explain why the edge has never been found, or ships don't fall off it! There are whole towns of such odd-thinking people. This

is very strange for we know the earth is round.
There is no question about it. It has been measured.

A peek inside the earth

Let us see what we know about this round earth.
It is made of layers surrounding a central core, like
the stone in a peach only rounder. The core may be
liquid. It is probably very hot. But we cannot be
sure of these things. None of us has been there!
Miss Inge Lehmann of Denmark, one of the world's
great earthquake scientists and a onetime lecturer at
the National Academy of Sciences in Washington,
has shown that there are both inner and outer parts
of the core. However, that important discovery will
not concern us now.

The core extends out a little more than half way
toward the surface of the earth. Outside it is the
mantle, with rocks in a very different condition,
though we don't know much about them, either. It
makes up most of the rest of the earth, filling it out
almost to the surface. It may also be divided into
separate parts.

The part we do know something about is the surface layer called the crust. Under the loose dirt and
gravel that lie in many places, and the topsoil we
dig into for our gardens, lies solid rock. It is partly
sedimentary rock, made by the hardening of silt,

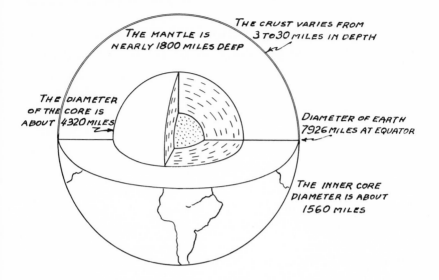

The seismologist's concept of the structure of the earth.

shells, and the skeletons of prehistoric animals, that have settled in old seas and lakes. It is partly other rocks that have hardened from melted minerals in the earth, much of it thrown out by volcanoes.

How the Moho got its name

The fact that the earth really has a crust was the brilliant discovery of a Yugoslav scientist named Mohorovičić. He wondered about the peculiar pattern of vibrations reaching his station from a 1909 earthquake in Croatia. Seeking an explanation, he reasoned that there is a distinct lower boundary to the surface rocks. Underneath, in the mantle, is quite different material, which carries the vibrations faster than do the rocks near the surface. Scientists call such a boundary a discontinuity, so in this important case it was named for its discoverer — *Mohorovičić Discontinuity*. Busy scientists call it the *Moho*.

Everything above the Moho is the crust. The name crust gives the idea of a rough-grained covering, and that is just what the earth's crust is. Travelers in the mountains can see this very clearly. There the crust is badly mixed up and twisted into all sorts of shapes.

Considering the size of the earth the crust is quite thin — thinner in proportion than an apple skin. Under the oceans it is no more than three to five miles thick. Under the continents it is twenty miles or more. This is quite a difference, and one might wonder why.

The crustal rocks are lighter, having floated to the surface in the long periods of earth formation. The continents and the mountain ranges are like ice floes and icebergs in the sea. They are masses and lumps of the crust floating over the heavier mantle rocks. Where they stand higher, their feet are deeper because of their weight. So we find the Moho deeper under the continents, and especially deep under the mountains. The deepest parts are *roots of mountains*. They are sometimes fifty miles down.

Nature's balancing mechanism, known by the impressive-sounding name *isostatic compensation*, provides that with time and under sufficient pressure, the rocks are forced into new forms, shaping themselves into mountains and valleys, continental highlands, and sea depths.

The rocks of the crust have radiated their heat until they are now cool and brittle. They have broken in many places, leaving the long, deep cracks that we call faults — often breaking with such violence that we call them earthquake faults. The earthquakes that wreck cities and crack open the countryside are reminders of great forces at work, changing things in accordance with some grand design of Nature. There are many reasons for the squeezing and twisting of the rocks.

Great forces at work

Chemical reactions and radioactivity inside the earth can cause heating and flowing of the inside materials, as if they were liquid. This may cause pressure against the crust, and change its shape. Volcanoes build up pressure in pockets of melted

rock, or break out as Parícutin Volcano did in a
Mexican cornfield in 1943, to pile mountains of lava
in new places and load down the crust.

The melting of the glaciers that covered much of
the northern lands in past times has taken away such
weights of ice that the crust has been springing up,
or rebounding, ever since. In America the Great
Lakes basin is tilting southward in a rebound following the retreat of the last ice field ten thousand
years ago. Precise surveys show this. An important
earthquake area has developed in the St. Lawrence
River valley. There an uplift is going on, as shown
by old sea beaches that can be found seven hundred
feet high on the hillsides near Montreal.

Boston and New York have few earthquakes, but
they are sinking a foot a century, as proven by sea-
level recordings. The ground under those great cities
participates in the grand design of Nature — a design based upon never-ending change.

Probably the most important natural force at work
to disturb the crust is the weight of earth material
moved from place to place by river flow. Mountains
are worn down by erosion. The rocks crack when
freezing and thawing. They wear away under the
chemical action of water, the blast of blowing sand,
and the grinding action of glaciers. Then the material goes as silt and gravel to the sea. Great val-

leys like the Colorado River's Grand Canyon are the hollows left after rivers have eaten away the land.

All this takes time, but there is all the time in the world — millions and billions of years. And the mass of material becomes very great. The Mississippi carries into the Gulf of Mexico each year enough solid matter to make nearly two square miles of new land where the sea once tossed.

Mountain ranges transported to the sea to build deltas like those of the Nile and the Mississippi overload the earth's crust and make it bend down. Perhaps that is what happened in the Mississippi valley a century and a half ago when large areas of bottom land near the Mississippi sank in the New Madrid earthquake. The crustal rocks must have been under tremendous weight from the sediments brought there by the rivers from half a continent. During long periods of time the mud from the Appalachian and Rocky Mountain highlands gradually filled what was once an inland sea covering much of our central valley lands.

These are forces far beyond any human power to change or control. Yet, strangely enough, man has actually produced small-scale crustal bending of his own. He didn't intend to, but that is what happened at Hoover Dam, near Las Vegas, Nevada. It holds back Lake Mead, a vast collection of water where there was none before. When the Colorado River poured forty billion tons of its water into the lake — enough to fill a 230-ton swimming pool for every person in America — the crust just had to sink under the weight. Small earthquakes began. A Government observatory was set up by Dean Carder, of the Coast and Geodetic Survey, who spent years studying them to see if they were a danger to the dam. Fortunately, they weren't. Hoover Dam is perfectly safe.

The overloaded rocks

Bending and breaking and the formation of faults has taken place almost everywhere. Some of the faults reach the surface and can be seen as broken ground. Most of them are buried by thousands of feet of sediments and rocks. The average depth of earthquake centers is supposed to be twenty miles, but a few are much deeper, even hundreds of miles down. This shows that the rocks are brittle even in the heat and pressure of that mysterious region. But there is a limit. Earthquakes have not been known to be more than six hundred miles deep. Probably they cannot occur any deeper because the heavily squeezed rocks are forced to act somewhat like liquids, and cannot break as they would at the surface.

The pressure inside the deep earth, particularly near its center, is so tremendous that we cannot match it in a laboratory. The weight of all the earth bears down. The thousands of miles of heavy rocks, the seas, the mountains, our tall buildings, even big trucks on the highway and bulldozers on the construction jobs — all press down on the insides of the earth. No one can imagine what such pressure does to the atoms and molecules of the rocks.

It must be hot, too. We know it gets hotter as we go down in mines. We see volcanoes spilling out molten rocks and fire. How hot it is we don't know, but there's enough chemical and radioactive energy to explain any amount of heat.

Part of our difficulty in trying to understand conditions inside the earth springs from the fact that we do not know about the creation of the earth. Until this is explained, there seems to be no way to know what it is like down there.

The fact that earthquakes are generally somewhat near the earth's surface gives us a better chance to understand them. When one does happen, the jerking of the rocks extends throughout a considerable zone of weakness. It often reopens cracks left by older earthquakes. Generally the rock on one side of a fault breaks away and moves sideways, or up and down along the fault, until the tension is released. Everything comes to rest in a new position, and there it will stay until stress has built up again.

The broken earth

The first definite knowledge that faulting is associated with earthquakes grew out of the famous Rann of Cutch shock of 1819 on the coast of India. A vast area of low plain on one side of the fault sank below the sea. Along the other side, for perhaps eighty miles, the earth sprang up to heights as great as twenty feet. Since that time surface faulting has been found after many strong earthquakes.

Such a vertical displacement creates a bank or step in the ground, called a scarp. When this happens time after time through the ages, the bank grows higher and higher until it becomes a geographical barrier known as an escarpment. Such one-sided mountains are found in many places, even under the sea. Some extend hundreds or thousands of miles from end to end. The eastern face of the Sierra Nevada in California is an escarpment, although weathering and erosion partially conceal this identity. Africa's Great Rift is marked by a spectacular wall of high cliffs frowning down on the valley of Lakes Tanganyika and Nyasa.

The Ancash earthquake of November, 1946, was

marked by a new break on the Quiches Fault cutting across the Peruvian highlands among the Andes. In this remote region Enrique Silgado and his assistants traveled twenty-five days on horses and mules to inspect the central area of the earthquake. They found a pair of scarps two miles apart, with the land between sunken ten feet. The greatest height of scarp they found was about twelve feet.

In 1955 the Seismological Society of America, meeting at Reno to discuss the problems of earthquakes, adjourned to permit the members to travel a hundred miles east into the Nevada desert to view the effects of a recent strong earthquake. As they approached the place they found the pavement of U.S. Highway 50 cracked where a fresh fault crossed the road. The painted center line, always before straight as a string, was offset to make a jog of several inches! The cracked earth of the desert showed where the fault extended right and left of the road.

High on the side of Fairview Peak, after a breathtaking climb, the scientists beheld a bank of earth and gravel twenty feet high, cutting across the hills and valleys. The ground on the west side of the fault had risen to a new level. This was perhaps the greatest single upheaval in the earthquake history of the United States excepting Alaska.

Fairview Peak did not, however, have the greatest

Twenty-foot scarp caused by the 1956 earthquake at Fairview Peak, Nevada, the greatest vertical faulting in one earthquake ever noted in the continental United States excepting Alaska.

split on record. During an 1899 earthquake near the Fairweather Mountains of southeast Alaska, the rocky shore of Disenchantment Bay jumped out of the water in the greatest single movement ever known anywhere. It rose forty-seven and a third feet in one earthquake!

Measuring this height required some clever work. There were no previous sea-level measurements in the locality, so other kinds of evidence had to be found. They included traces of elevated beaches, old high-water marks on the rocks, and telltale effects on the vegetation. The best evidence, found some years later, was the remains of dead barnacles far out of the water. Vertical measurements between the highest live barnacles to be found and the highest dead barnacle shells did the trick.

Such readjustments of Nature will happen again and again in that very locality, because the land is rising. We know this through sea-level measurements. They show a rise of nearly five feet in the past fifty years. But future earthquakes may happen on different faults and with different effects. Scientists cannot predict when and where they will be.

Not all the sudden movements of the earth can be so easily explained. On February 17, 1931, two weeks after the Hawkes Bay earthquake in New Zealand, workmen on an island in Sponge Bay near Gisborne watched a boulder-bank rise seven feet out of the sea without warning nor any signs of tremors. A two-acre island was formed where the water had been two feet deep at low tide! Delayed actions of such kind make first-class mysteries.

The unbelievable San Andreas

Not all faulting is vertical, and not all earthquakes produce scarps. Slipping on the San Andreas Fault in California is nearly all horizontal. It is no less damaging, as the tragedy of 1906 at San Francisco proved. The fault cuts across California's country-

Broken fence where the San Andreas Fault slipped in the California earthquake of 1906.

side in a line nearly seven hundred miles from a point near Mexico to its disappearance in the sea north of San Francisco Bay. The land on the west side of that fault slipped twenty-one feet northward in the 1906 earthquake, moving two mountains ten feet farther apart, offsetting roads and fence lines and the rows of trees in orchards, and even cutting the walkway between the road and a man's front porch!

Harry Fielding Reid, of the California State Earthquake Investigation Commission, suspected a grand march of large regions of the earth, creating tension between the regions. He suggested that the earthquake was the release of the strain slowly accumulated over the years. There had to be a break sooner or later, and this was it! This idea, known as the *elastic rebound theory*, is widely accepted, although it is still doubted by some who prefer to think the faulting is the *result* of the earthquake instead of its *cause*. Anyone may take his choice of these ideas. American seismologists agree with Reid.

Restless lands

Measurements by Government surveyors have shown that Reid was right. A large region west of the San Andreas Fault is creeping slowly northward at about two inches a year. This may not seem much, but in time it does place stress on the crustal rocks until they finally break. It has happened time after time through the ages, and in all that time the creep of the land has become very great. One can see this on aerial photographs which show streams with thousands of feet of offset where they cross the fault — the total effect of many earthquakes.

The San Andreas Fault from the air. Two old streams at upper right have had their valleys offset by repeated slipping of the fault during thousands of years. The other streams are younger.

Geologists have discovered even more exciting proof. Matching rock formations have been found on opposite sides of the fault, at places no less than 350 miles apart. They must have been joined at one time — perhaps ten million years ago. One wonders how many earthquakes it took to add up to all that distance.

Ocean survey ships have used their instruments to identify undersea rocks by their magnetism. In this way scientists have found similar displacements along a number of faults under the Pacific Ocean west of California. Ocean surveys years ago disclosed the faults as submarine escarpments.

The Mendocino Escarpment, one of the great breaks in the earth's crust, is a mile-high wall cutting nearly two thousand miles of the sea floor west of Cape Mendocino. Matching rock formations have been found more than seven hundred miles apart on opposite sides of this fault. This surprising fact became known after long search by Coast and Geodetic Survey ships, and careful study of the magnetic recordings by workers at the Scripps Institution of Oceanography at La Jolla. The matching of the rocks was a triumph of scientific sleuthing.

In the light of such discoveries, many scientists are now ready to think more carefully about an old and almost incredible suggestion of the seventeenth-century English philosopher Francis Bacon, who presumed to take *all knowledge* as his province. Bacon's suggestion, later elaborated by A. Wegener but long scorned by scientists, was that the continents have drifted, in the life of the earth, like icebergs, far across the face of the globe. A common argument is the strikingly close fit between the Atlantic coastlines of Africa and South America. This is thought to indicate that they were once one land, having broken away and drifted apart to create the Atlantic Ocean.

How the Mohole got its name

While earth scientists are settling geographic problems of such magnitude, let us not forget the importance of the earth's deep insides. The Moho is so invitingly near the surface that earth scientists long thought of the day they would drill through it, to see what rocks are in the mantle, and their condition.

There are new developments in deep oil drilling, and new skills of drillers in putting wells down from platforms at sea, where the crust is thinnest. Taking advantage of these drills and tools, a group of American scientists who call themselves the *American Miscellaneous Society* are drilling where the thinnest crust can be found. Already, of course, it has been named *Mohole*. What new knowledge of the earth will come from this difficult and bold undertaking? It is even possible that something will be learned to realize that old and so far hopeless dream of science — how to predict earthquakes.

IV

Where Will the Next Earthquake Be?

In Nature's infinite book of secrecy,
A little I can read.
— SHAKESPEARE

The Greek language, which provides many of the
roots of English, has the word *seismos* for earthquakes. Robert Mallet, an Irish engineer of a century ago, coined the words *seismology*, for the science of earthquake study, and *seismologist*, for those
engaged in it. The first syllable is pronounced like
"size."

People ask seismologists about these natural
events that are so hard to understand. They most
want to know when and where an earthquake will
strike. The seismologists wish that they knew the
answer.

The search for Nature's secret

Nicholas Heck, a modern writer on earthquakes, says that their most impressive characteristic is their unexpectedness. Heck has expressed one of the basic facts of seismology: he has told us in effect that we cannot predict earthquakes.

However, scientific curiosity is endless, and men will keep on studying the problem. They try to understand forces at work in places deeply hidden in the earth. We have seen how they invent difficult experiments like the Mohole project, seeking a glimmer of new knowledge. They also look for new laws of Nature that can be read from the scramble of earthquake happenings.

Perry Byerly, a leading seismologist of the present time, has said that in seismology, as in other fields of science, the value of any natural law that may be discovered lies in its use as a means of prediction. He did not promise us a law by which we can predict earthquakes.

If there is one, perhaps it is waiting to be recognized somewhere among the details of earthquake history. That story will tell us where and when earthquakes have happened in the past. It will show us a pattern of activity that we can expect to continue into the future. So — where have earthquakes been, and where are they now?

Unfortunately, much earthquake history is highly uncertain. Old earthquake lists are incomplete and do not agree among themselves. The period of observation varies widely from some four thousand years in parts of China to two thousand years in Europe, and in America we have but four hundred years of it. Only in the present century — within sixty years, that is — have we had information about shocks in ocean areas. This is because modern instruments were needed for that purpose. There are remote areas like Antarctica where important scientific work has been possible only in very recent times.

This kind of unbalanced history gives false importance to some areas, simply because we have better information for them. It is still true, however, that we have much historical material, and very good maps of the areas most often shaken by earthquakes. With good ideas of their past frequency, we may guess how frequent they will be in future.

Belts of weakness girdle the earth

The major earthquake areas are long narrow belts spaced widely about the earth. There are at least three, though various experts describe them in different ways. Probably half of all known shocks have been in a great belt including the countries surrounding the Mediterranean Sea and the lands east-

ward from there through Asia Minor and the Hima-
laya mountain region of southern Asia toward the
Pacific Ocean. Here this great belt broadens and
joins another which almost completely encircles the
Pacific. The strong earthquakes of New Zealand,
Japan, Alaska, California, and western South America, are all in this circum-Pacific belt.

Another important but lesser belt is marked by a
range of submerged mountains extending from the
Arctic Ocean down the length of the middle Atlantic
to a point deep in the Southern Hemisphere. The
scientific interest attached to this feature of the
earth is very great.

We find these three great regions, and some small
secondary belts and detached regions, covering the
most important mountain chains on earth. One of
them includes the Himalayas, highest of all. In them
we find also most inland seas including the Mediterranean, Red, Caspian, and Caribbean. In them we
have also the chains of oceanic islands known as
island arcs. The Aleutians, Kuriles, West Indies,
and Hawaiian group, are island arcs. Such island
groups are geological curiosities and puzzles, noted
for their earthquakes and volcanoes. They lie near
deep ocean waters where crustal changes are going
on. They are usually in curved chains — hence *arcs*
— and appear as the tops of volcanic peaks grown

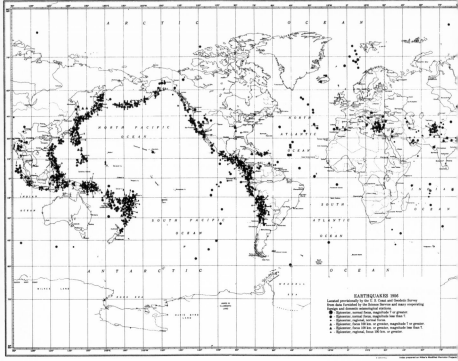

*World earthquakes located by the Coast and Geodetic Survey
in 1956. Even the shocks of one year alone have a pattern
disclosing the belts of greatest earthquake activity.*

out of the upper edges of tilting blocks of the earth's
crust.

Many of the great mountain chains lie alongside
seacoasts bordered by deep ocean trenches. The
steep slopes between the mountains and the ocean
depths are scenes of crustal change and mountain-
building, punctuated all too often by earthquakes.
Many of the mountains are volcanoes — some dead,
others alive to spew ash and lava over the land.

On looking at maps of the Pacific belt earthquakes, the Japanese seismologist Omori remarked how well they outline the western coasts of the Americas. This is indeed true, though most geographers would look on Omori's suggestion as a most unusual way to construct maps!

Wegener, one of the authors of the drifting continent theory, explained that the earthquake belts illustrate a great pattern outlining the earth's zones of weakness. A British seismologist, H. H. Turner, a man of undoubted imagination, thought the Pacific Ocean, surrounded by its earthquake belt, was the void left when a great chunk of the earth had broken loose and flown off into space to become the moon. This, of course, would have been in the youth of the earth, long before the time of man. Scientists do not think much of Turner's idea, however they must admit such a separation would have left cracked and weakened belts behind.

The Pacific belt, with somewhat less than half of all known earthquakes, has been said to release four-fifths of all earthquake energy. If so, it must have stronger shocks on the average than other areas. The people of Peru, Chile, and Japan, patient sufferers from strong shocks, would probably agree without question.

Mountains we never see

The long chain of mountains forming the mid-Atlantic Ridge is the source of many fanciful tales about an ancient continent called Atlantis. It is thought to have existed long before history began, then to have sunk in the sea. The ridge has long been the object of exploration and persistent probing by scientific research ships of several countries. One American ship from the Woods Hole Oceanographic Institution, of Massachusetts, proudly bears the name *Atlantis.*

The chain is completely submerged but for a few high points. We can see standing above the water the islands of Iceland and the Azores in the North Atlantic, and Ascension and St. Helena far to the south. There are connections under the waters south of Africa and Australia to other submerged ridges in the Indian and Pacific Oceans. They all form the longest mountain system on earth.

Down the crest of the Atlantic Ridge is a deep cleft, in places fifteen to twenty miles wide and a mile and a half deep. This unusual wrinkle is not fully understood despite the thousands of sounding probes dropped into its recesses by the oceanographic explorers. It may be a crack where the earth has pulled apart. In any event, it is the source of the mid-Atlantic earthquakes, so we know it is a place of weakness.

Even within the belts we have described there are many places where there are no records of earthquakes. There must be many such places, for half of all recorded earthquakes today occur in places where none were ever known before.

Safe area — perhaps

The large regions outside the belts are the so-called quiet areas. They have few earthquakes, even in many places very near the belts. The largest of all is the Pacific Ocean basin itself, almost completely surrounded by the circum-Pacific belt. This fact does not seem to agree with Turner's theory about the origin of the moon, for one would assume that such a violent rupture as that would leave the whole area weakened and shaky. Other seemingly safe areas are the centers of continents, in such lands as Canada, Brazil, Central Africa, and Australia. People in those places don't remember earthquakes and believe that they will never happen. They may be very wrong!

An earthquake can happen anywhere — and if you can wait long enough it does. A violent shock struck eastern Canada and New England in 1663. Boston was damaged in 1755. New Yorkers may feel secure, but in 1929 some of them felt the tremors of one of history's strongest shocks, only eight hundred miles away near Newfoundland. It was under the fishing grounds called the Grand Banks, and it broke twelve transatlantic cables, costing millions of dollars, and sent fifty-foot sea waves into nearby bays.

Even the British Isles and Australia have had earthquakes. In the United States there have been at least two great shocks no one would have expected. One was the Charleston, South Carolina, earthquake of August 31, 1886, the only disastrous one to visit the southeastern United States in historic time. And who would have thought that one of the greatest of them all would have torn at the quiet valley lands of the Mississippi, near New Madrid, far from any mountains or the sea?

How deep in the earth?

Most persons never think of how deep an earthquake may be, but it is an important point to scientists. Even in practical ways it makes a difference. Earthquakes very deep within the earth are likely to have much less severe effects than those near the surface. This is simply because they are farther away, although their effects may be felt over wider areas.

Scientists are much interested in the somewhat rare *deep-focus earthquakes*, as much as six hundred miles down in the earth. They are far below any of man's mines or drill holes. Their study may provide important clues to the condition of mysterious rocks men will probably never see.

Deep-focus earthquakes indicate fault zones dipping downward into the mantle, far below the crust, where they outline active mountain-building areas. They seldom occur outside the Pacific borders, where the Andes and other mountain chains stand forth. The deepest of all have been under the Tonga Islands — half-submerged mountains rising from the floor of the southwest Pacific Ocean.

Seismicity — a measure of the risk

After this look at where the earthquake zones are found comes the important matter of just where and how often the earthquakes happen at particular places in those zones. In a practical way it is important to people to know the risk they run. The building of the Golden Gate bridge, one of the longest in the world, was delayed over arguments about the amount of earthquake danger. It was very near the point where the San Andreas Fault crosses under the San Francisco Bay entrance.

Those planning to build houses, bridges or dams,

or anything that could be wrecked by an earthquake, naturally wish to avoid the worst danger
spots. Insurance companies, which charge premiums
for earthquake coverage in areas like California,
need to know what the risk really is. So we use the
evidence of history to find the *seismicity* of a locality.

Seismicity is the word used to indicate the liability
of any given place to have earthquakes. It is an
appraisal of the danger. Seismicity is high in Calabria, a small district in southern Italy which has
had twenty ruinous earthquakes in three centuries.
It is high in Concepción, Chile, which has been destroyed repeatedly by shocks associated with the
nearby Andes Mountains. The Japanese scientist S.
Hatai made Japan's place in the picture clear when
he reported between 4500 and 12,000 Japanese
shocks each year.

The late Beno Gutenberg and Charles Richter, of
the California Institute of Technology, prepared the
monumental book *Seismicity of the Earth*, the most
complete study of the earthquake zones of the earth
yet published. All important earthquakes of modern
history are classified by locality and strength. Very
good comparative ideas of earthquake risks of dif
ferent world areas are given. This has great value
to people living near earthquake zones, but it

gives no clue to the prediction of individual earth-quakes.

They come in families

We find by experience that the strongest earth-quakes are often in groups, repeated shocks follow-ing in rapid succession. Sometimes there will be several of almost equal violence. Most of the great shallow earthquakes do in fact have such a pattern. This is one reason why they are so destructive when they hit inhabited areas. The later shocks finish off the buildings weakened by the earlier ones. How-ever, even if we could be sure of this, it would be a poor kind of prediction to foretell the finish of what is already started.

Strong earthquakes are often preceded by a defi-nite string of increasing foreshocks. They are much like the aftershocks following such great earthquakes as the one at New Madrid, but of course in reverse order. One might suspect that these foreshocks, some of them days or even years ahead, could be looked on as reliable forewarnings.

Unfortunately, earthquake foreshocks are not very useful for this purpose. No one has ever discovered any reliable pattern to go by. We may remember the great Kwanto earthquake in Japan, which was preceded by several years of mounting foreshocks.

In 1922, after a particularly strong one, Professor Omori of Tokyo Imperial University proclaimed the worst was over. He thought they had had it all by then. And this was just one year before the great disaster.

The difficulty is that no one can tell what the foreshocks mean, or when they will end. They often remain small, with nothing of importance to follow. So one never knows whether they are foreshocks or not. To make it worse, deep earthquakes often have neither fore- nor aftershocks.

Averages and intervals

One important fact about earthquakes, that seems to have become a natural law, has great scientific importance. Hugo Benioff of the California Institute of Technology demonstrated that the average release of energy the world over stays about the same year after year. A period of unusually violent or frequent shocks may then be followed by a year or two of comparatively mild activity. This interesting idea tells us something of the overall activity of the whole earth, but it certainly has nothing to do with the timing of individual shocks.

The search for revealing patterns is made more interesting by a tendency of truly strong shocks to follow fairly regular intervals. However it usually turns out that the intervals are neither sufficiently regular nor dependable. Byerly has pondered long over the known history of San Andreas earthquakes near San Francisco. There is a strong popular tradition that they repeat themselves at regular intervals, the commonest guess being fifty years. But Byerly found it quite impossible to determine a definite repeat rate, or even to decide which were really major shocks. He and others have guessed at various intervals between forty and seventy years. Not much can be made of this vague information. Byerly asked, "What are geologists to do with such a cranky and erratic earth as ours?"

So we find our store of historical information tells us where earthquakes have occurred, and may perhaps occur in future. We can even guess that they will occur with some regularity in active areas. Foreshocks may lead us to suspect something, but there's no certainty about it, and certainly no exact idea as to when it may be. We have not yet read much of Nature's secret!

A confusion of faults

Visible faults appeal to us because they can be examined. We can see what has happened to them after they have broken in earthquakes. It is like the problem confronting aircraft experts who examine the wreckage of a crashed plane trying to find what caused the accident. It works, sometimes. So scientists are directly interested in the faults, although there are many difficulties in the way.

The deep-focus earthquakes show no surface faulting at all. In fact, the majority of all faults are forever hidden, countless numbers of them, alive and dead, crisscrossing deeply buried rock layers. Of those we can see, there is but poor relationship with known earthquakes. Most California shocks, for instance, seem to be associated with the Coast Ranges, but there are many other faulted areas in California where none occur at all. Many faults of great age have no reputation for ever having moved. Actually most are long dead, but we can never be sure. The only proof that a fault is active is that someone saw it move — and there is no proof at all that one is dead.

The creep of the land can be measured

Possibly the most promising approach to earthquake prediction is to watch what happens to the land near active faults. In the San Andreas area it has actually been measured, as we have said. The story of its land movements is long and well known.

Measurements of the distances and directions between survey monuments in the area were made by Government engineers before 1906. After the calamity at San Francisco they reworked the survey to see how much the land had moved. The results were not too clear because of a lack of enough points, yet it was certain that the distances between points on opposite sides of the San Andreas had changed. Those on the west had certainly gone northward — some of them perhaps twenty feet. Surely it was no coincidence that the largest road and fence offsets in the earthquake had been about that much.

The surveyors, wanting to know what was going on, have repeated their work at intervals. So they found that the regions on the two sides of the fault are indeed slowly drifting past each other at about two inches a year.

Perhaps twenty feet was what it took to cause a break. Two inches a year would make twenty feet in a hundred years. Is this a clue? Would the San Andreas break again about 2006? Perhaps, but the history of the fault does not seem to prove it at all. Byerly's study found no regular time interval between San Andreas earthquakes, though it seemed less than a hundred years, if anything.

Byerly also pointed out another difficulty. The

fault does not act at all as a well-behaved fault should. It broke in 1857 at Fort Tejon, near Los Angeles. The 1906 break was hundreds of miles to the north. One wonders about the condition of the fault between those places. It ought to be in severe stress, but who knows? Perhaps we will in time, as the surveyors continue their work. Certainly more earthquakes will occur.

Tilting occurs too

Another evidence of a straining crust is tilting of the ground. This, too, can be measured, but it is slight and extremely difficult to detect. It requires delicate tiltmeters. They have been tried in both America and Japan. The American tests have not proven anything except that changing weather and rainfall cause some tilting effects in the ground.

Japan has had more positive success. Ground tilts have been measured near active faults noted for their frequent earthquakes. Using their knowledge of this effect, in combination with the timing of the shocks, clever Japanese scientists have made surprisingly close advance guesses of new shocks. This method has therefore seemed to have at least some success in particular places.

It has often been suggested that sensitive listening instruments in deep wells might "hear" warning noises in the rocks. The idea has not been tested effectively. Even if it would work, an impossibly large number of instruments would be needed to keep track of all the places where earthquakes might happen. Many seismologists wish a few wells could be drilled for instruments to keep track of one large fault, perhaps the San Andreas near San Francisco. It would be expensive, certainly, but perhaps the greatest difficulty is that many people simply won't spend money on it, believing that earthquakes cannot ever be predicted.

Looking for the trigger

Not so the scientists — both the serious ones and the crackpots and opportunists who would have us believe they are scientists. Having failed to discover a law based on observation of earthquakes themselves, they seek to find predictable causes of earthquakes. These may be obvious or farfetched — it depends on the determination and honesty of the seeker.

Perhaps the most common idea is to find natural forces that might trigger earthquakes. It is supposed that when earthquakes are about ready a little extra force would make the strained rocks let go.

This seems so obvious a method that it has always appeared to me a shame it doesn't work.

Everyone knows about gravitational forces, and how important they are in earthly events. The sun and moon have attraction enough to produce the ocean tides. These are long bulges in the ocean, raised by those attractive forces and caused to travel around the earth as it turns. In some bays the tide attains a height of fifty feet. Forces capable of such results should have an effect on the solid earth as well. This they do in fact, making an earth tide in spite of the stiffness of the rocks. The ground rises and falls at New York or Washington in varying amounts between six and eighteen inches twice every day! The force to do this might seem quite enough to trigger earthquakes.

This very promising idea must have been in the mind of an Italian, Pignataro, who made a long study of the aftershocks of the Calabria earthquakes of 1791 in southern Italy. He found an interesting relation between the times of the aftershocks and the positions of the moon. So he believed the moon was triggering them! A later worker named Perrey actually stated a law based on Pignataro's list, by which the aftershocks were supposed to be most numerous when the moon was directly overhead or directly down under. Supposedly it didn't matter which way the force was acting. He said also that the changing rate of aftershocks clearly indicated the moon's major period of motion through the heavens, every 29.6 days.

Perrey's law is extremely interesting, and perhaps important if it is actually true. To find out if it is, there have been many investigations. H. E. Stetson of the United States reported a buildup of earthquake activity at the times of certain moon positions. Omori found that nearly all of sixty-five land earthquakes in Japan occurred within one hour of high or low tide, which is of course related to the moon's position. Unfortunately the investigations of many later men have failed to confirm these occurrences in any general sense. Perrey's "law" apparently cannot satisfy Byerly's definition of usefulness.

The tide and coastal loading

If the direct force of gravity cannot be convicted of triggering earthquakes, what then of its indirect effects? The heavy load of sea water on the coast changes as the tides rise and fall. Seismologists have recorded slight tilting of the earth toward the sea when the tide was in. R. C. Hayes of New

Zealand found a tendency for aftershocks of a 1950 earthquake to coincide with a falling tide and subnormal barometer. The frequency of small tremors in the Himalayas seems to increase at times of flooded rivers — another extra load on the earth's crust. However, none of these ideas have ever been proven to the satisfaction of scientists.

If the strong gravitational forces of the sun and moon cannot be related to the timing of earthquakes, certainly the much weaker forces of the distant planets cannot be. Yet this is just what many unscientific persons tell the world, as if they were announcing some clever and great discovery. It is no new idea. Conrad of Megenburg tried unsuccessfully in 1359 to relate earthquakes to the positions of the planets in the sky. Uncounted others have since tried. Somehow the configurations of the planets seem to excite popular interest and to impel amateur predictors. Perhaps it is the influence of our many astrologers, whose tricky stock in trade is the planets and their motions.

The atmosphere, animals, and other things

Gravitational attraction, from whatever source, is not the only natural force that has been blamed. Varying atmospheric pressure due to changing weather may seem slight to those without sensitive instruments. Its effect over large areas, however, may be great enough to produce important forces. Some think there is a slight tendency for earthquakes to be more frequent with rising or falling barometers, but I think this may be doubted.

Another possibility for earthquake prediction is the earthquake vibrations from distant shocks. Interesting coincidences in the timing of far-separated earthquakes have often been noted. The North African shocks of 1755 followed by mere minutes the tremendous Lisbon earthquake, but there is no scientific reason to show that they were related to it.

There are still other things people wonder about. Unrest and excitement of animals just before strong shocks have often been noted. This might be a way of getting very brief advance notice, but it would hardly be reliable nor sufficiently early to do any good. The effect on animals may be caused by slight vibrations that humans do not notice. But animals also get excited about numerous other things, such as extremely high-pitched sounds in the air that people cannot hear.

Then you may take your pick of a host of other things — atomic bomb explosions, hot or cold weather or thunderstorms, or all the queer ideas we discussed in Chapter II. None of them will help. We will have to wait for the new scientific discoveries before we can predict earthquakes.

How to stop earthquakes

All this does not bother the many people who say they can do it. Some are simple and honest, with only the ability to deceive themselves. Others are charlatans. Unfortunately, these people are not easily exposed. It is almost as hard to disprove a worthless theory of prediction as it is to find the true causes of earthquakes. There are thousands of earthquakes daily on earth, mostly very slight. Overeager or dishonest men can find earthquakes that seem to prove almost any theory and fulfill any prediction. They never give up trying to show how clever they are, but all they accomplish is to make nuisances of themselves. Scientists prefer to base their thinking on plain facts and simple logic.

Father Joseph Lynch, the well-known Jesuit seismologist of Fordham University in New York, has complained of cranks who not only bothered him about earthquake predictions — they have even threatened the Fordham authorities with violence if they wouldn't remove Lynch's observatory to make him stop *producing* earthquakes!

The New Zealand seismologist Eiby has said that

practical men want real answers to their question, "Where will the next earthquake be?" Until they know, they shouldn't build their houses on fault lines. This obviously true statement has queer significance for me, for I know what Perry Byerly did! He, who doubtless knows more about San Francisco area earthquakes than any one else, had to choose a house near the Berkeley campus where he teaches. The one he selected lies but a few feet from the Hayward Fault, the second worst fault in the area, and one with a bad record indeed. From his windows it can be seen across a narrow road. Is he a practical man?

Perhaps we can see in Byerly's choice an expression of his belief that one place in an earthquake area is as good or bad as another. Certainly predictions do not mean a thing. Heck was right. The most important characteristic of earthquakes is their unexpectedness. And if we can read a little in Nature's book of secrecy, it certainly isn't much as far as earthquake predictions are concerned.

V

Spreading Waves
of Earthquakes

Their cause is hidden, but our woes are clear.
— OVID

Beno Gutenberg was strolling one day on the campus of the California Institute of Technology, deep in talk of earthquakes with his longtime friend Albert Einstein. As they walked there occurred the earthquake of March 10, 1933 — a disastrous shock at nearby Long Beach. Perhaps because they were moving instead of standing, or perhaps because of the intensity of their talk, neither noticed the motion of the ground.

This was the more surprising because it was a strong earthquake, felt by almost everyone in Pasadena. Neither man had ever felt one, though Gutenberg was known to wish for such an experience.

This was too much for Mrs. Einstein. Her first

remark to Mrs. Gutenberg was: "What do you say about our two *dummkoepfe* — they always wanted to experience some earthquake and here they were in the middle of one and they didn't even feel it!"

Mrs. Einstein was exercising her wifely privilege. She knew well enough, while calling the two men thickheads, how brilliant they were. They proved it in everything they did. Gutenberg, after hearing of the first atomic bomb test of the Crossroads experiment at Bikini Island in the Pacific, had remembered an explosion of old war materials in Germany in 1945 that had been recorded in England. Rushing to his sensitive instruments in the laboratory, he had found the tiny wiggles in the lines of his recording. They meant the ground vibrations had come nearly six thousand miles across the Pacific to announce their arrival at Pasadena. He was the first to report that important fact.

What it takes to shake the ground

Even small explosions cause tremors in the earth, as do earthquakes. The tremors from quarry shots and construction blasts have been studied repeatedly by seismologists. They were particularly important at Ross Dam, a magnificent high structure in the Cascade Mountains where power is generated for the lights of Seattle During its construction water tunnels had to be blasted through the rocky sides of the gorge. Government seismologists recorded and studied the blast vibrations penetrating the fresh concrete of the dam to be sure no harm was done, nor the dam weakened.

Such studies were made at the Panama Canal, where the foundation rocks were thought to be weak in an area of new construction. It was necessary to discover the effects of the lock gate movements and machinery vibrations. The foundations of delicate machinery at atomic energy plants, and of tracking instruments at missile launching sites, have been examined to find how stable they would be during earthquakes or in the shock of rocket launchings.

Natural events also shake the earth. The tremendous explosion of Krakatoa Volcano in the Sunda Straits of the East Indies in 1883, one of the most violent outbursts of Nature ever known, sent tremors into the ground. They were slight, as it happened, for most of that burst of energy went upward into the air. Five cubic miles of earth and rocks were thrown up as dust. The sound was heard a thousand miles away.

In 1908 many awed and frightened Siberians watched a brilliant object coming from the sky and breaking up in a violent explosion thought to have been three miles high. The air blast destroyed the forests for miles around, then passed completely around the earth. The ground vibrations were recorded hundreds of miles away at Irkutsk. Although it has been known as a meteorite, Russian scientists have proclaimed this spectacular space object a comet.

Machinery, automobiles, railroad trains, and other things may shake the ground. Who hasn't heard the windows rattle when a heavy truck passes the house? One seismologist warned a visitor not to be concerned about certain wiggles on his earthquake record; all they meant was that the 5:15 train was on time four miles away. Even the air can make the ground tremble. Strong winds hitting a hillside can do it.

For all these reasons seismologists make every effort to find quiet places to put their instruments and do their work, where they hope not to be bothered by these disturbances that do not mean earthquakes. The best places are on real bedrock, but of course this cannot be found everywhere. Excellent results have been obtained on top of ice sheets miles thick in Antarctica. But ice is really a kind of rock, after all.

The distances that vibrations and tremors will travel depends much on the material they are in.

Thunder, which seems so violent when you are near it, can be heard only a few miles through the air. Explosions and disturbances in the ground make themselves felt at great distances. Our sensitive instruments show us that strong earthquakes shake the entire earth.

Elastic vibrations

The tremors are really vibrations, which may occur in any elastic material. The earth rocks are elastic, being strong and rigid. They are like the metal in a bell, or the strings on a guitar or ukelele, or a diving board at the swimming pool. All these are elastic and when struck, or plucked, or jumped on, they vibrate in motions that die down slowly. So it is in the earth. Sharp disturbances set up elastic vibrations in the rocks.

When the rocks vibrate the motions become waves spreading outward in the fashion of the ripples that spread out when a pebble is thrown in a pool. Elastic waves may sometimes appear on the surface of the earth, but they are very different from the water ripples. They form themselves in trains quite capable of penetrating the entire earth.

The tremors were first recognized as elastic vibrations by Professor John Mitchell of Cambridge, England, after he had studied the effects of the Lisbon earthquake. This was a new idea then. It has explained many things since.

Fast waves and slow

After a long study of an earthquake of 1857 at Calabria, Italy, the Irish engineer Robert Mallet advanced the beginnings of scientific seismology by investigating the speeds of the earthquake waves. He used gunpowder shots to make his own artificial waves in the ground, timing their arrivals at a distance by watching for the shivers they made in a bowl of mercury. Much has been learned of the speeds since Mallet's day. They vary in different parts of the earth, but in general they are quite well known.

The earth is not simple like a guitar string or a bell. Its tremors and wave trains are very complex. Some waves are so short and high-pitched that people do not feel them. Sometimes they arrive ahead of the strong waves and disturb animals in the zoos before people notice anything. This happens because some animals are able to feel and hear with great sensitivity. The Japanese have found that catfish may become sensitive and restless even several hours before an earthquake. Perhaps this is from unnoticed foreshocks.

Some of the high-pitched waves have the right

frequency to make the sounds we hear coming from the earth. However, other noises may be due to rubbing or squeezing of the earth particles as the waves pass. They are sometimes loud like shots, sometimes more like distant rumbling. Many have said it is like a truck running over cobblestones. In the Assam earthquake of 1899 a deep roar was heard two seconds before the shock struck.

Then there are longer, slower-pitched, and much more violent waves. These are the ones that wreck buildings and change landscapes — that leave the devastation that we hear so much about. It is the lurch of these waves that starts landslides and triggers volcanic eruptions.

Waves in the earth are the evidence we have of earthquakes in remote regions, so their study has become the main business of seismologists. By now we know much about them and their complex manners. We will not try in this book to learn all about earth waves, but it will help to know a little about the principal ones.

The fastest, therefore the first to arrive anywhere, are the primary waves. They are a train of pressure waves — vibrations like those of sound waves in the air, but slower pitched. Seismologists call them P-waves. As they pass an observer the pressure in the ground increases and decreases every second or two. While this goes on the particles of the ground dance back and forth along the line from the earthquake center. The front of this wave train is an expanding sphere within the earth, growing outward at speeds averaging five miles or so a second.

P-waves go through all materials, including ice and water, and even air. They penetrate nearly the entire earth when they are strong enough, stopping only when their energy is exhausted. They can be reflected, like light from a mirror, or refracted as by a lens, on striking a layer of rock with different elastic nature. This has been our means of investigating the internal structure of the earth. It is this reflection of waves that helped us discover the roots of mountains, of which we have read. The roots deflect the waves, leaving dead areas, or "wave shadows."

One layer that sends back echoes of earth waves is the famous Mohorovičić Discontinuity, or "Moho," between the crust and the mantle below. Another is the boundary between the mantle and the core, nearly halfway to the earth's center. Miss Lehmann's brilliant discovery of the inner and outer cores involved the discovery and explanation of very faint wave echoes from that obscure boundary. This is part of the reason for her very great fame, which she carries in a charming and modest way. She is one of two women seismologists I have known, and there ought to be more. It is interesting work.

After the P-waves come the secondary waves, at a slower speed of about three miles a second. They have shear or shake motion, so they are called S-waves. The earth particles move back and forth in a sideways motion like that of the wave that runs along a stretched rope when it is struck. S-waves are usually a few seconds apart, for they vibrate less rapidly than the P-waves. They can travel the same paths, and be reflected from rock layers, but they cannot go through fluids. This is because shear waves involve a change of shape and require rigidity, whereas fluids can hold no shape whatever. They are not rigid.

S-waves do not go through the earth's core, and it is therefore believed to be liquid. At any rate, it acts as a liquid. We cannot be sure; we cannot even imagine what the rocks are like in that region of great heat and enormous pressure.

There are still other waves. The so-called L-waves are much longer than the P- and S-waves. They vibrate only three or four times a minute, or slower. Though complex, they are composed chiefly of two types, named for their discoverers. Love waves agitate the earth particles in a sideways shaking motion like that of the S-wave. Rayleigh waves are

WAVE MOTIONS CAUSED BY EARTHQUAKES

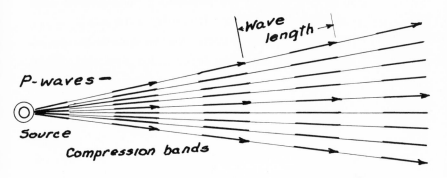

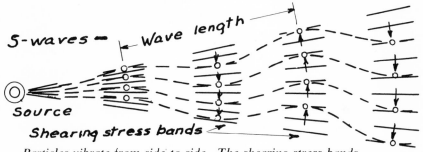

Particles of rock vibrate in lines from the source. It is not the particles, but the compression bands, which travel outward.

Particles vibrate from side to side. The shearing stress bands travel outward.

The particles move sideways as in the S-wave motion, and also in little orbits as shown.

the most elaborate of all, having a kind of round-about dancing motion of the particles in vertical, nearly circular paths.

All we need to know about the L-waves is that they travel only on the surface of the earth and at even slower speeds than the other waves. They produce the largest ground motions and make the most vivid parts of the earthquake recordings. They often do the greatest part of the damage. Some have been known to travel the earth from end to end with such persistence that they were still recording on seismographs after four days or more.

Since these various waves travel quite definite paths and speeds outward from their starting point, they can tell us something of what happened to send them. They are messengers, coursing through the inner space of the earth, bearing news of earthquakes. How shall we read these messages from hidden places?

VI

Keeping Track of Earthquakes

Hear thou, read, mark, learn, and inwardly digest them.
— BOOK OF COMMON PRAYER

How to spot earthquakes without instruments

Two men in a car near Helena, Montana, were startled to see large earth ripples coming toward them across the fields. The ground was actually rolling. One cried out, "Look, it's an earthquake! Must be coming fifty miles an hour from over there by the hills!" They may have been the first men, by a few seconds, to know of the disastrous Helena earthquake of October 18, 1935.

Two friends were talking on the telephone in New Zealand when one broke in, "The ground is shaking. It must be an earthquake!" His friend felt nothing at the moment, but had hardly said so when he also felt the tremors. Talking it over, they agreed that it must have come from somewhere behind the first man — out back near a place called Cheviot.

These people were engaging in a sort of simple seismology. Certainly it was not very scientific. Experts who have instruments can see the different kinds of wiggles on their record paper, knowing which is which and the exact moment each arrives.

Locating the quake

The most important single fact about the wave travel is that the P- and S-waves have separate speeds and reach distant stations at different times. The farther they have come, the longer is the time between their arrivals. Almost everyone is familiar with the common trick of counting time between a lightning flash and the arrival of the slower thunder, to learn how far away the flash was. In exactly the same way, good estimates can be made of the distance from the earthquake by finding the time between the wave arrivals.

Seismologists commonly start from such simple information to estimate where an earthquake occurred. They know the distance quite well. It is far more difficult to judge the direction, although rough guesses are possible when records from dif-

HOW SEISMOGRAMS ARE READ

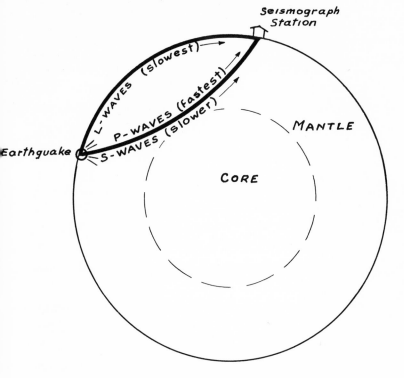

At the station the seismograph pen, or a light beam, moves along a line on the paper, recording the waves like this —

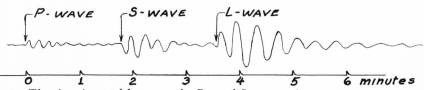

The time interval between the P– and S– waves is a measure of the distance of the earthquake from the station.

Locating an earthquake. Telegraphic messages reporting the distances of the shock from several seismograph stations are used to plot the location, even when it is under the sea.

ferent kinds of instruments are compared. As a matter of fact, long experience sometimes permits seismologists to guess the general location of an earthquake simply by the appearance of the record he obtains. Though very complex, it often shows similar details from all earthquakes of that locality.

The exact plotting of an earthquake location usually requires distance information from three or more different stations shown on a globe or earth model. Because of this need, seismologists the world over are great cooperators. They always hasten to send records to one another, often by telegraph. There can be only one place which lies at the correct distances from the three stations. There the earthquake must be, and seismologists can be sure of it even if the place is far out under the ocean.

When we were at war with Japan, and the news wires were all closed down, military leaders were interested in Japanese earthquakes found out by such a method. They knew that great earthquake disasters might affect Japanese military power.

Instruments are essential

The science of seismology could not advance without the information we get from instruments. Many earthquakes are altogether too weak to be felt by people. In any event people are poor reporters, even when they do feel the shocks. Many become sick or unusually nervous. This is natural. One of the strongest of human faiths is that old Mother Earth is solid and immovable. It is a tremendous shock to people to have the ground move under them without warning. In many parts of the world nothing could be more unexpected and unusual. So most people are too upset to realize clearly what is going on. But they are deeply impressed and the experience is most likely to remain an outstanding event in life.

There are exceptions. I will never forget being in the Dominican Republic with a colleague, Harold McComb of the Coast and Geodetic Survey, who had spent much of his life designing seismological instruments. In a speech at the University he told of this, adding as a joke that never in his life had he felt an earthquake. He would like to. A day later we were together with several of the professors when a slight shock gently rocked everything about us. The professors, after a moment of alarm, smiled knowingly at McComb. He looked puzzled. Later he asked me privately what had happened. Was it an earthquake? He hadn't felt anything!

Perhaps I should have told him of a chap in Seattle who thought he knew well what an earthquake was like. He had felt numbers of them in his years in the Philippines and Alaska. He had just returned from many months of duty on a surveying ship in the northern territory. The stormy seas had made him insensitive and indifferent to rolling and swaying motions. From a deep sleep far in the night his wife waked him in excitement.

The house was creaking. The brooms hanging in the closet were swinging.

"It's an earthquake!" she screamed.

She will never stop reminding him of his sleepy-eyed protest, "I don't feel any earthquake!"

I know she won't. It happened to me. But I never thought to tell poor Mr. McComb.

The Japanese, who go through many shocks, might well be among the first to laugh at us both. Some of them, it is said, even boast of their ability to sense an earthquake in advance, like predicting the weather by how one's bunions feel.

All of this does not mean that the experienced seismologist doesn't use his eyes. He does indeed, judging the character of the waves by the effects he sees. These can be very interesting and full of meaning. Chimneys falling in certain directions, or gravestones toppling in rows like fallen soldiers, give good indications of the wave directions. Stones thrown out of the ground, as in the Assam earthquake, give proof of strong upward motions of the earth. Even the pattern of cracks in the ground or in masonry buildings can be very useful.

Stone monuments sometimes stand twisted about on their bases so as to face in new directions. This might seem to indicate some kind of circular motion of the ground, but engineers have explained that certain straight-line vibrations can do this strange trick.

There is a limit, in spite of all this, to the value of human observation. As we have suggested, people have many faults as observers. Instruments have no human faults. Neither do the waves in the earth, whatever their queer actions may be. Instruments are reliable and more sensitive than people. They give full pictures of the wave trains.

Good instruments have existed only in modern times, though we have historical accounts of early attempts to make them. The ancient instruments are interesting to us now mainly because of the fanciful decoration and imaginative ideas in their design. They had little scientific value. They indicated earthquakes, but could not measure their effects. It is the modern idea of measurement that has brought seismology from an art to an important branch of earth science. There used to be many cooks who practiced cookery as an art. They could never say how much flour and salt went into a cake. "Enough" was all they were able to say. Some of them made wonderful cakes, too, but it would be hard to imagine modern bakeries or food factories turning out their goods without means for measurement. It would be impossible to carry on scientific seismology without measuring instruments.

Beginnings of instrumental seismology

Perhaps the earliest known earthquake instrument should be called a *seismoscope* instead of a seismograph, because it indicated without measuring. It was invented, according to one historian, by Chang Heng, the Director of the Chinese Bureau of Almanac and History, A.D. 132. Chang, with typical Chinese inventiveness, constructed a highly decorated copper jar of barrel shape, three feet across. Around its sides he fitted eight dragon heads, each holding a ball in its mouth. Below each ball he stationed a frog, holding an upraised open mouth. Inside the jar hung a pendulum, like a bell clapper, arranged so that if the ground shook the pendulum would swing and knock one of the balls out into a frog's mouth. Perhaps this device would work when people couldn't feel the ground move, but it may be doubted. At any rate, it was supposed to tell which direction the waves came from according to which ball was down. This showed the direction to the center of the earthquake.

In the day of Chang, before systematic scientific ideas became common, things that could not be understood were subjects of mysticism, and elaborate

Seismoscope invented A.D. 132 by Chang Heng. A ball suspended within the instrument would swing when there was an earthquake, knocking a ball out of a dragon's mouth into one of the waiting frog's mouths. This kind of instrument can tell only of very strong shocks, and only roughly of their directions.

ideas had to be invented to satisfy the mind and curiosity. Chang's instrument consisted of dragons and frogs because they were symbols of mystery, standing for the Earth and Heaven. An earthquake is earthly, but produced by the will of Heaven. However, the device told little and fell into disuse for hundreds of years until it was rediscovered by later scholars.

Much later, in 1703, a Frenchman named de Hautefeuille used a bowl of mercury with eight lips about its sides, and with little cups under the lips. The shaking of the ground would slop the mercury, making some of it run out into a cup. This idea was the same in purpose as Chang's dragons and frogs, and it gave just about as much real information. Surprisingly, however, the idea has never completely faded from sight. In recent years there have been people here and there, without money for real instruments, who have hung pointed pendulums over bowls of sand so that their swinging would make marks in the sand to show the direction of the waves.

In the late nineteenth century there were any number of clever devices intended to tell when an earthquake had occurred. They would stop clocks, flash lights, ring bells, and do such other little tasks, but none could measure the waves, nor help much to tell where the earthquake was.

Pendulums are mentioned repeatedly where seismographs are concerned. This is no accident. The problem is of course to measure the movement of the ground at the observing station. But when the whole earth is moving, how is the measurement made? From what starting point?

The answer is probably not due to anyone's cleverness. It comes directly from our common knowledge that loosely hung objects try to stand still when things start moving about them. It is shown by the passenger straps in a streetcar, which hang backward when the motorman puts on the power to start the car. We see it when we jerk a drinking cup. The water wants to stay still, and slops backward out of the cup. So it is the *inertia* of a hanging pendulum — its tendency to stand still — that gives us a fixed or nearly fixed point to measure from. Most seismographs work on this principle.

Pendulum seismographs have been known many years, but for long they were not satisfactory. They were entirely mechanical. The need to attach something to a pendulum to draw the line on the paper spoiled much of its sensitivity and accuracy. When measuring tiny effects from distant earthquakes, they were not free to do a good job. Like Mr. Mc-Comb, they lacked sensitivity.

To overcome this, pendulums were made heavier and heavier, until seismologists bragged about the great weight of their instruments. Twenty tons was not uncommon. These monsters were very cumbersome, and still not sensitive enough.

About 1855 the Director of the Vesuvius Observatory, Luigi Palmieri, developed a so-called electromagnetic seismograph, which, however, bore no relation to anything now existing, and is today considered of no importance.

In the mid-1880's John Milne, one of the important figures in the history of seismology, invented a distinct improvement using photographic paper for the recordings. This reduced friction. He also installed a moving record paper, with clock signals automatically inscribed on the line with the wave marks. This improved the timing. Unfortunately his magnification was insufficient, and the paper did not move fast enough, so his timing was still not sufficiently accurate.

Then came Galitzin!

One of the master strokes in advancing the science of seismology came from the fertile mind of a Russian. The Russians have always been important leaders in this field. Even the most notorious of them all was a worker in seismology. I found present-day scientists at Tiflis, in the Georgian Soviet Socialist Republic, proudly showing the desk and writing implements where Josef Stalin tabulated the records of the Tiflis seismograph. They were proud in those days. Stalin, known as Dzhugashvili, was a young man believed destined to become a humanitarian and benefactor of the people. That, I learned, was all they admired of Stalin, for the deeds of his later life are despised by the Georgians. Stalin really contributed little to seismology.

Back to Galitzin. It was he, Prince Boris Galitzin of Lithuania, who found a better way to do things. So he made himself one of the all-time great men of seismology.

He was for some reason rejected by Russian scientific workers, so he went in a huff to exile at Strasbourg, France, where one of the great seismological laboratories of the world still stands. There he found sympathetic workers and a rich atmosphere for his creative work.

His great idea — the one that brought the science of seismology out of darkness into light — was to place a coil of fine wire on the pendulum, then to let it swing between the poles of a magnet. Thus the mechanical burden on the pendulum was removed. When things moved around it, it stood beautifully still, and the moving magnet generated a small electrical current in the coil. This follows the famous principle of magnetic induction developed by Faraday in the middle of the nineteenth century, and now used in all electric generators. Galitzin's current drove a sensitive electrical indicator called a *galvanometer,* and thus made a true record of the waves. It was a simple idea which the world had awaited for many years.

Courtesy Coast and Geodetic Survey

A seismograph recorder. The pen moves when an electrical signal is generated by the seismometer during an earthquake. The large drum turns around each half hour, and each time around it moves along the shaft to keep the lines separated. The moving pen writes the "signature" of the earthquake.

Truly modern seismographs

The story of the seismograph is long and complicated. It has come far from the simple idea of Galitzin. Some kinds now use electric eyes. Some combine Galitzin's electrical system with Milne's idea of photographic recording. Some use pen-and-ink recorders to "write" the record, and some use magnetic tape. They all have electrical systems, and the magic of electronics means that they are sensitive and accurate. Some now make records on which the ground motions are magnified hundreds of thousands of times! Even modest-sized earthquakes in far-away China are recorded clearly in New York, London, and other places anywhere on earth.

The simple pendulum hanging down from a pivot has been improved by supporting it in a nearly horizontal position. It stands out to swing like the gate in a fence. The advantage of this is to slow down its natural swinging time, making the pendulum even more steady. Of course it should stand as still as possible to measure the true size of the earth motions.

A single seismograph pendulum works in only one direction, and cannot tell the full size of wave motions in other directions. To overcome this single-mindedness of the pendulums, well-equipped stations today are arranged to show the parts of the wave moving north-south and east-west, each on a separate instrument. This combination helps, but not with certainty, to show the general direction of the wave travel. When you read in the paper that the seismologist at Fordham University has recorded an

McComb-Romberg horizontal seismometer. This old-fashioned instrument has a weight on a boom which is pivoted at the base of the pedestal and held horizontal by the wires. In this kind of instrument the end of the boom moves in the field of a horseshoe magnet, generating a small electrical current which operates a separate recording system.

SIMPLE IDEAS ON SEISMOGRAPHS

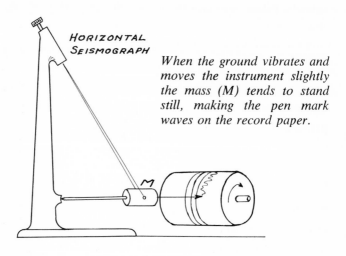

HORIZONTAL
SEISMOGRAPH

When the ground vibrates and moves the instrument slightly the mass (M) tends to stand still, making the pen mark waves on the record paper.

When the ground vibrates up and down the spring-suspended mass (M) lags behind the motion, making the pen record the waves.

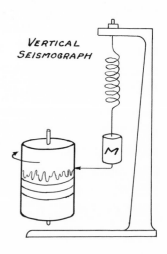

VERTICAL
SEISMOGRAPH

earthquake and estimates its location to be in some remote place like South America, you may be sure that Fordham has this combination of instruments.

The well-equipped station also has a vertical instrument, in which a weight resting on a spring tends to stand still and record the up-and-down motions of the ground. This completes the observation of the principal facts about the waves as they arrive at the station.

Seismographs without pendulums have also been found useful. One kind is called a *strain seismograph*. This clever instrument, developed largely by Hugo Benioff of California, does not directly measure the motion of the ground. It is a long bar set to straddle a stretch of bedrock, where it becomes a measuring rod to show the stretching and squeezing of the rock as the waves pass through it. Its length must never change if it is to measure correctly, so its temperature must be kept uniform. It is therefore kept in a cave or tunnel, which usually costs a great deal. But it has advantages. It gives good records of extremely slow waves which take a longer time to pass than one could expect a pendulum to stand still. Such waves may take many minutes to pass.

Now, with modern instruments, it is possible for man to know and study all strong earthquakes throughout the world. This does not mean all earth-

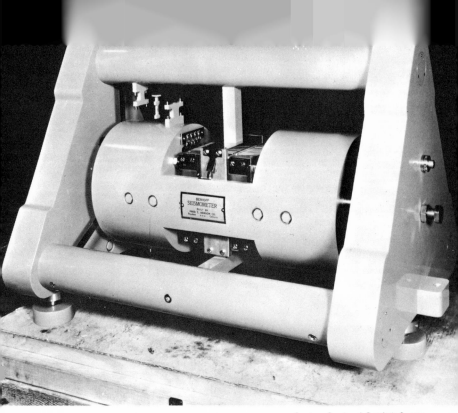

A modern Benioff seismometer. This highly sensitive instrument will detect many more earthquakes than older types. The central cylinder is a heavy mass that lags behind when the frame of the instrument is moved by vibrating ground, even when the motion is microscopic in size. An electric current is generated which operates a recording system.

quakes, for most of the million or so every year are so small that only supersensitive and nearby instruments can detect them. There are as yet only two or three regions on earth where this favorable condition yet exists. One of these is California. The

University at Berkeley and the Institute of Technology at Pasadena operate first-class networks of instruments. Possibly there will be so complete a story of the California earthquakes in time that a pattern will become clear from which predictions can be made. But much work and study remain.

The location of an earthquake is not our only concern. Another is the depth below the ground. The center, where it starts, is called the *focus*. Knowing where this is helps us understand what kind of an earthquake has taken place, and something of the earth's interior at that place. Probably the most important fact about an earthquake, besides where it happened, is its strength. The scientific importance of the shock depends very much on this. It may be great, even though far from people and cities.

Seismologists are deeply interested in the faulting action — that is, how far and in what direction the rocks slipped. To know this much about events on a deeply buried and forever hidden fault may be remarkable, yet progress is being made. The complex markings of seismograph records may some day be unraveled so we can know these details. Then better predictions of great sea waves from submarine earthquakes will be possible. Engineers may make safer buildings. Certainly we will have gained some new understanding of our earth.

Putting the waves to work

Man in his cleverness has found many special uses for earth waves. The most important is the search for oil. Small earth waves made by "shooting" underground explosives can travel to receiving instruments laid out nearby. These are small simple seismometers called *geophones.* The waves arrive in definite patterns which show the paths they have traveled and the reflections they have made from buried rock layers. Thus man sends his own little messengers into the ground where he cannot go, to report things he cannot see.

After a survey of a large area, with many shots and full study of the recordings, the shapes of rock layers deep in the earth can be plotted. Geologists have learned that certain rock formations, particularly dome-shaped ones, are likely to have oil pools trapped under them. Finding the formations and the domes by sending the wave messengers is much cheaper than drilling hundreds of wells to find out. It has led to the discovery of many rich oil pools.

Before the development of this method of *seismic prospecting,* important new oil deposits were found in America at the rate of only about one a year. Then in 1924 a large Texas dome was found by seismic methods. From three hundred feet deep in the earth it delivered three million barrels in ten years, handsomely repaying the company which trusted the seismic prospectors. The method worked so well that other companies took it up, and for ten years afterward new pools were found at the rate of eight a year!

Finding hidden secrets in the earth

Seismic prospecting works equally well at sea, the little waves going down through the water to seek out the rock layers under the sea bottom. Domes have been found deep in the sticky muck under the Gulf of Mexico. Today many *Texas Towers* stand in the Gulf waters many miles from the Texas and Louisiana shores, where oil wells are giving up more of the fuel needed for American automobiles and airplanes. Some of the wells have been drilled in ground forever hidden under two hundred feet of ocean water.

Seismic prospecting is useful too for the discovery of bedrock under the soil in places where construction works are planned. Contractors estimate the cost of excavating by this easy method, and they find where heavy foundations can safely be placed. Father Daniel Linehan, a Jesuit priest of Weston College, Massachusetts, dared to shoot dynamite charges amid the sacred surroundings of the Vatican in Rome, finding ancient forgotten catacombs deep in the ground. On a trip to Antarctica during the International Geophysical Year he helped the Air Force find the location of bedrock under a proposed new runway at McMurdo Sound. Then he flew to the South Pole itself. There the American scientific camp huddles, half buried on an almost endless plain of snow and ice, nearly two miles above sea level. That is two thousand feet higher than the windy peak of Mount Washington in New Hampshire. How much piled-up ice was there under the camp?

Measurement of its thickness was difficult, but after several trials by Father Linehan and others, it turned out that the ice extended all the way down to the level of the sea. The sound messengers were able to go down and bounce back, through nearly two miles of ice, and still mark their return on the instruments at the top.

Even thicker beds of ice have been found near the United States Byrd Station in western Antarctica. At one place it is near three miles in thickness, lying on bedrock a mile and a half below sea level! Scientists have in fact found the bottom of the ice to lie below sea level in many places in Antarctica. If the climate warms up a million years from now, and the ice all melts away, Antarctica will be a group of islands — not a solid continent at all. Seismic prospecting has told us all this.

Microseisms

No account of earth waves would be complete without a look at one kind of very puzzling little wave, mostly a nuisance though possibly useful at times. It jiggles every part of the earth regularly, day and night, every few seconds. These strange quivers are called *microseisms* because of their small size.

They were discovered early in the period of instrumental seismology. By 1872 an Italian, Bertilli, had decided that the tiny movements of a pendulum in his basement were related to changes in air pressure. How right he was! By 1900 the Jesuit Father Algue had studied them in the Philippine Islands, associating them with Pacific Ocean storms. In 1909 a worker in Samoa tried to predict storms by noting when the microseisms increased in size. In spite of this and other work, they were rather poorly understood before Galitzin's time, for most old mechanical seismographs could not record them. Even today they present many unanswered problems.

Most seismologists can tell when a weather front is coming, even if they don't listen to the weather man, because the recordings show an increase of mixed-up microseisms of all sizes and vibration rates. Sometimes these quivers make a complete smear all over the record. Seismologists call it "hash." It might be due to strong winds striking the ground as the storm front approaches, or more likely from some kind of air pressure waves beating against the ground.

Microseisms seem to come more regularly from the sea than the land. Most seismograph stations near the coast are particularly troubled by them. It has been thought that they might be due to the breaking of surf on the beaches, but this does not seem to be systematic enough. They are probably the result of some kind of rhythmic wave actions, either in the water or in the air above it. Some storms at sea, and particularly hurricanes, cause very active and regular microseisms.

The Navy, assisted by the Coast and Geodetic Survey, ran tests during several recent years, hoping to find a reliable method of finding and tracking tropical hurricanes through microseism-watching. Arrays of instruments in Florida and the West Indies were able to show from which directions the microseismic waves were coming, and for a time it seemed that the method would succeed in pointing out storms at sea. A few storms were actually found this way.

Unfortunately, more work made the results seem quite uncertain, and the investigation was stopped. In any event, the Weather Bureau started searching for hurricanes by airplane search-flights, so perhaps the seismographs were not much needed for this after all.

Microseisms are an ever-present plague for seismologists. Where they occur strongly they impair seismograph records so it is impossible to do fine work on true earthquake records. The best earthquake recording stations are in places where waves are very small, and one of the first interests of earthquake scientists is to find such places. Generally, areas far from coastlines are best. In the United States the Government found one of the best possible places, near Albuquerque, New Mexico, to build a seismological laboratory.

Earthquakes and bomb tests

Beno Gutenberg detected the effects of a distant atomic explosion. Uncle Sam's scientists have used instruments since then to study the ground effects of almost every American atomic test. They have kept track of the tests made by the Soviet scientists. It is the only useful method of detecting atomic explosions in underground caverns. Unfortunately it is difficult to tell the difference between the earth waves from such tests and from small earthquakes, so the United States is studying earthquake effects as never before. Modern instruments of the highest class have been furnished free to a hundred or more seismograph stations the world around, and millions of dollars are being spent on scientific studies of the resulting records. We want the waves to tell the truth, and we want to be able to recognize the truth when we see it. This is probably the biggest research effort ever made in the history of seismology.

Seismology in the space age

Earthquake waves, as we have seen, tell about the unseen insides of the earth according to the way they are transmitted and reflected between an earthquake and the recording station. Scientists believe that a study of moonquakes could tell things about the structure of the moon, if they could only set down a seismograph there. At least there are no oceans of water or air on the moon — probably there would be no microseisms! But is the moon growing or shrinking, and changing as the earth does?

Since knowledge of this kind might unlock some of the secrets of the universe, the National Aeronautics and Space Administration is planning to send a seismograph to the moon by rocket. Scientists at Beno Gutenberg's old seismological laboratory in California are working on this problem. They have designed a rocket-borne seismograph which will signal its wave messages back to earth by radio.

One wonders what Galitzin, and even Gutenberg, would have thought of this idea!

VII

How Big Can an Earthquake Be?

Until we can measure the things we talk about, or express them in numbers, our knowledge is meager, indeed.
— LORD KELVIN

Is the rumbling of a truck over the cobblestones an earthquake? Or the blast of dynamite in a quarry or at a construction job? How about the earth waves from an atomic test under that flat-topped mesa at the Nevada test site? These latter waves, at least, can go thousands of miles through the earth.

What is an earthquake?

These are earthquakes, if you mean merely something that makes the earth quake. In the literal meaning of the word they actually are. But by popular understanding and dictionary definition they are

138

not. Webster says an earthquake is caused by faulting of the rocks, or volcanic shocks. Even within this restricted meaning there are enough earthquakes, and more than enough, to keep us busy tracking them and measuring them for size.

Of the million or so earthquakes each year that are strong enough to register on nearby instruments, relatively few can be felt by use of the human senses. Several scores produce tragic effects somewhere on earth, and perhaps one or two are real catastrophes. Scientists are interested in all — the little ones as well as the great ones.

At least some of the million disturbances are very minor things. A few may be due to rock falls in limestone caverns or abandoned mines, though there may be some doubt whether these could be called earthquakes, under the definition. Others are violent bursting of pieces from the rock walls of mine tunnels, due to disturbed pressures in the rock. These events are *rockbursts,* and they are definitely earthquakes.

The need of a measure

Definition or no, these occurrences all produce earth tremors. The great earthquakes and the tiny shocks — all of them do. But they vary so in their effects that if one seismograph could record the greatest and the least, one would appear many millions of times larger than the other.

In view of all this difference in size, there must be a way of measuring so we can know what kind of earthquake we are talking about. Both engineers and scientists are interested in comparing different earthquakes, and in knowing the strength of each. But they go about it in different ways.

A scale of measurement is invented

Pignataro, the same Italian worker who thought he had discovered a connection between earthquakes and the position of the moon in the sky, actually designed a measurement scale as early as 1785. So did P. Egen of Germany some forty-three years later. Both men had the same good idea, but neither had enough information to create a satisfactory scale. So their scales failed to come into general use. By 1878, however, two other workers together designed a scale good enough to have survived. They were De Rossi of Italy and Forel of Switzerland. The Rossi-Forel Scale is still used in a few places. It describes the different earthquake effects that can be seen and evaluated by observers — things like chimneys falling and pavements cracking.

Another Italian, Mercalli, who had made a serious study of the timing of strong earthquakes between

1883 and 1901, felt that he needed a more accurate way to describe them. He designed his own scale of earthquake effects divided into twelve different degrees of violence. This has since been modified by other workers to suit their own ideas of different local needs. The Modified Mercalli Scale, unlike the broth that was spoiled by too many cooks, has succeeded. In one form or another it is used today by engineers and others who are mostly concerned with the damage effects of earthquakes.

All such scales are based on what happens to the earth or to man's buildings on earth, or even to man himself. For instance, some of the things described are the waking of people from sleep, fear and nervousness — even the reactions of animals. Eiby relates that the effects are often those most familiar to the local people, such as one used by the Observatory in Australia, which gives as one of the degrees on its scale "like a horse rubbing itself against the verandah post."

These and other effects that cannot be measured are full of information and quite useful, but they sometimes fail to satisfy scientists because they do not tell the strength of an earthquake — only what happened at some more or less distant place.

One seismologist called such scales nothing but horseback ratings of the shaking at a given place, judged by effects on buildings, crockery, women and children, dogs, horses, herds of elephants, or whatever. Grade II meant that few people felt the shock; IV that it rattled windows; VII that there was slight damage; X that it was destructive; and XII (the highest rating) that it smashed almost all structures to the ground, threw stones into the air, and (believe it or not) shot posts out of postholes!

I must confess I never saw a published scale with that last item, but it may have been used somewhere. The Modified Mercalli scale, as adjusted three decades ago by Harry Wood of the California Institute of Technology and Frank Neumann of the Coast and Geodetic Survey, is in general use now in the United States. I give it here in full so in case an earthquake strikes where you live you can check whether the news reports are correct:

MODIFIED MERCALLI SCALE OF 1931
(ABRIDGED)

1. Not felt except by a very few under especially favorable circumstances. (1 Rossi-Forel scale.)
2. Felt only by a few persons at rest, especially on upper floors of buildings. Delicately suspended objects may swing. (1 to 2 Rossi-Forel scale.)
3. Felt quite noticeably indoors, especially on upper floors of buildings, but many people do not recog-

nize it as an earthquake. Standing motorcars may rock slightly. Vibration like passing of truck. Duration estimated. (3 Rossi-Forel scale.)

4. During the day felt indoors by many, outdoors by few. At night some awakened. Dishes, windows, doors disturbed; walls make creaking sound. Sensation like heavy truck striking building. Standing motorcars rocked noticeably. (4 to 5 Rossi-Forel scale.)

5. Felt by nearly everyone, many awakened. Some dishes, windows, etc., broken; a few instances of cracked plaster, unstable objects overturned. Disturbance of trees, poles, and other tall objects sometimes noticed. Pendulum clocks may stop. (5 to 6 Rossi-Forel scale.)

6. Felt by all, many frightened and run outdoors. Some heavy furniture moved; a few instances of fallen plaster or damaged chimneys. Damage slight. (6 to 7 Rossi-Forel scale.)

7. Everybody runs outdoors. Damage neglible in buildings of good design and construction; slight to moderate in well-built ordinary structures; considerable in poorly built or badly designed structures; some chimneys broken. Noticed by persons driving motorcars. (8 Rossi-Forel scale.)

8. Damage slight in specially designed structures; considerable in ordinary substantial buildings with partial collapse; great in poorly built structures. Panel walls thrown out of frame structures. Fall of chimneys, factory stacks, columns, monuments, walls.

Heavy furniture overturned. Sand and mud ejected in small amounts. Changes in well water. Persons driving motorcars disturbed. (8+ to 9− Rossi-Forel scale.)

9. Damage considerable in specially designed structures; well-designed frame structures thrown out of plumb; great in substantial buildings, with partial collapse. Buildings shifted off foundations. Ground cracked conspicuously. Underground pipes broken. (9+ Rossi-Forel scale.)

10. Some well-built wooden structures destroyed; most masonry and frame structures destroyed with foundations; ground badly cracked. Rails bent. Landslides considerable from river-banks and steep slopes. Shifted sand and mud. Water splashed (slopped) over banks. (10 Rossi-Forel scale.)

11. Few if any (masonry) structures remain standing. Bridges destroyed. Broad fissures in ground. Underground pipelines completely out of service. Earth slumps and land slips in soft ground. Rails bent greatly.

12. Damage total. Waves seen on ground surfaces. Lines of sight and level distorted. Objects thrown upward into air.

This is a so-called *intensity scale*. It hasn't any particular right to that name, but seismologists decided long ago that it was as good a name as any, so we may as well accept it. The rating found for any place depends much on its distance from the earthquake. It also has much to do with the nature of the earth's crust and the topsoil in the vicinity, but we don't understand these effects very well.

What the locality has to do with earthquakes

Sir William Hamilton, British envoy to the Italian port of Calabria, reported in 1783 that buildings on soft ground suffered more than those on hard ground or rock. He paid tribute, I think, to the Biblical parable about the danger of building your house on the sands. The earthquake of July 28, 1957, near Taxco and Acapulco, Mexico, did moderate damage at those places, solidly built on rocky hills. But at Mexico City, several times as far away, the damage was severe, with sixty-eight dead, and a repair bill of perhaps twenty-five million dollars, enough to rebuild completely many a small city. This is because Mexico City sits on deep beds of soft mud where there was once a lake. This soft mass shakes very much like jelly in a bowl that is jolted. Such loose shaking of the foundation is much harder on buildings than the sharp vibrations found in solid rocks, a matter that has long been understood by engineers. It is quite probable that had Mexico City been founded by modern engineers instead of by the

Aztec Indians of the fourteenth century, it would have been placed somewhere on firmer ground.

This shows what mistaken ideas one can obtain about the real strength of an earthquake. A tremendous one far away in a deserted area may do no harm to anyone. On the other hand, an insignificant shock in the earth directly under a city may create a sensation far out of proportion to its scientific importance. It happened a few years ago to the old Inca city of Cuzco, in Peru, which was severely damaged while other Peruvian towns felt hardly anything. An interesting result of the Cuzco shock was the destruction of modern masonry buildings — that is, ones built in the recent centuries since the Spanish conquest — while ancient Inca stone structures stood undamaged. And this is the more remarkable since the Incas used no mortar between the stones. The secret was the skillful use by the Indians of great massive stone blocks very beautifully fitted together in an extremely strong interlocking manner.

Maps of intensity

Engineers and building officials and others interested in the effects of earthquakes can get valuable information by studying area maps showing earthquake intensity ratings. The maps are usually drawn with lines outlining the zones of different degrees of earthquake intensity.

It was not always easy to do this. A German worker named Noggerath was first to attempt to make such maps after he studied an earthquake of 1846. He did not, however, have reliable intensity reports to plot on his maps. Nevertheless his maps were useful in indicating the localities of earthquake centers, this being long before the day of instruments capable of showing such details.

In the present time, to get enough intensity reports from many places, public officials and other persons willing to help are organized in reporting teams. With many reports, useful maps can be made. The lines outlining the zones are then accurate and reliable. Sometimes they are nearly like circles, in cases where the shock energy spreads equally in all directions. The larger circles outline areas of lesser damage. When the character of the rocks causes the shock energy to expand unequally in different directions, the curves may turn out to be very lopsided or elongated. Whatever their shape, the curves are known as *isoseismal lines*. They are "lines of equal seismal intensity," if you care for a technical definition. The map is, of course, an *isoseismal map*.

Insurance companies are among the users of such maps. They use them to learn the earthquake

danger in areas where property owners want earthquake insurance. Knowing the risk, the insurance
people are able to charge correct premium rates.
Scientists are interested in isoseismal maps because
they give information, not only about the earthquakes, but also about the hidden earth rocks of the
earthquake areas.

*Isoseismal map of an earthquake near Butte, Montana. Each
curve outlines the area having an intensity rating shown by
the figures beside the line. Such a diagram indicates the wave-
carrying quality of the earth's crust in different directions from
the earthquake.*

Courtesy Coast and Geodetic Survey

The magnitudes of earthquakes

It is clear, nevertheless, that earthquake scientists have different needs than city engineers, newspaper reporters, and insurance men. They are interested in earthquakes as natural phenomena of the earth — things to be measured. They must have an idea of their real strength — not what happens somewhere at a distance.

It was only recently that earth science progressed to the point where a new kind of scale based on the earthquake itself could be developed. This remarkable achievement was due to the same two California Institute of Technology scientists we have heard so much about — Beno Gutenberg and Charles Richter. They developed a *magnitude scale,* now commonly called the *Richter scale,* which indicates the energy released by the earthquake movements.

Gutenberg and Richter used the simple fact that the strength of the earth waves depends very much on the energy of the earthquake. Stronger earthquakes make stronger waves, and the stronger they are the bigger will be the marks on the seismograph record. Modern instruments that have been standardized make records which can be measured to indicate the wave size and the energy of the earthquake — that is, the energy released at the center of the quake. The basis of this idea is of course modern standardized instruments. This means instruments of the highest quality that have been thoroughly tested in seismological laboratories.

The energy is usually spoken of in *ergs,* which are units of work. An erg is a small unit indeed — something like the work a housefly could do in one second. The number of ergs in a great earthquake would be represented by a 1 with about twenty-five zeros after it!

The name *magnitude* for Richter's scale has no more descriptive meaning than that of the other kind of scale — *intensity.* But it does seem to have something to do with the idea of size, and seismologists like it. Unfortunately, newspaper reporters are quite likely to become hopelessly confused about the meaning of these two words, so newspaper stories are often quite unreliable about the actual strength of an earthquake.

Richter's magnitude scale does not have grades like the Modified Mercalli Scale. It is numerical, with the numbers related in a fast-mounting way to the energy. What this means is that each number stands for 62 times as much energy as the previous one. Thus an earthquake of magnitude 7 (which is very great) would be 62 times as strong as one rated at 6. You can see that this kind of a scale can rise rapidly from nothing to very high values. Scientists call such a scale *logarithmic*. Used for earthquake rating, it can be used with decimal fractions, so an earthquake might be rated at 6.5 or 7.2, for instance.

The highest number ever known for an actual earthquake since modern instruments have been used has been 8.9, and this Richter magnitude stands for the earthquake we mentioned that let loose all those ergs with the many zeros in their number.

The strongest of all earthquakes

This value has been reached twice in the time of modern instrumental seismology — on January 31, 1906, for a shock off the coast of northern Ecuador, and on March 2, 1933, for an undersea earthquake east of northern Japan. Neither of these two tremendous spasms has any place in the popular literature of earthquake disasters, simply because neither occurred where it could wreck a city or kill thousands of people.

The great Himalayan upheaval of August 15, 1950, which tore the mountains apart and provided the most violent in our chapter on stories of famous earthquakes, was slightly below the limit. Its rating was 8.7. Another one, the San Francisco shock of

1906, is estimated to have rated 8.2. It was lower, therefore, than the Chilean earthquake of May, 1960, which has been assigned the rating of 8.5. There are definite differences in the energy of these earthquakes, but certainly they were all bad ones. The differences in their damage effects were entirely matters of chance. Their locations in relation to centers of population made all the differences in their effects.

Each of the largest known earthquakes, with the Richter rating of 8.9, let loose in the world about as much energy as twelve thousand atomic bombs like the one that ended the Japanese war with the destruction of Hiroshima. Much bigger bombs have been developed since, but it seems doubtful that any bomb ever made will shake the earth to match the effect of a great earthquake. The energy of a bomb does not all enter the earth, even when it is exploded underground. Much of it goes into heat and other forms of radiant energy. On the other hand earthquake energy is nearly all in elastic waves which do go through the earth.

It has been said by the Japanese seismologist Tsuboi that there is a greatest possible earthquake. Our American Byerly agrees. This is based on the obvious fact that the rocks in the earth's crust have only a certain limited strength. They can store only so much strain energy before they have to break. Computations seem to indicate that Tsuboi's "greatest" earthquake has already been seen in this century — twice in fact. The two shocks of Richter rating 8.9 will probably never be exceeded.

Softer, weaker rocks must exist in most places, for earthquakes of such great magnitude are certainly most rare. In places where shocks are fairly frequent, their usual strength is in most cases far below the greatest possible. This should be of some consolation, even to those living in earthquake areas.

Nicholas Heck, in his book *Earthquakes,* discussed the greatest possible shock of an area or place. He raised the question whether it could ever be said that a place had already seen its worst possible earthquake. After pointing out that few earthquakes wait until the full strength of the rocks has been reached, he concluded that a greater one would always be possible. You would not be safe in thinking the worst had yet been seen. Heck didn't seem too sure of this, however, for he then decided that an area with a long record of frequent earthquakes could be treated differently. In such cases there would seem to be good reason to suppose that the worst had already happened. For instance, San Francisco will probably never have a worse shock than that of 1906. I am not sure whether Heck meant this to be a comfort to the people of that city.

The earthquake rule of the world

The rule announced by Benioff and Richter stated that the earthquakes of the world tend to happen on a fairly uniform average level over the years. Of course this tells us nothing about the size of any single shock, but it does have important meaning about the total of all of them together. The fact that the total is somewhat constant seems to imply some sort of worldwide regulation — perhaps a relationship between all of them. Seismologists have not found any evidence of a connecting mechanism between earthquakes in different regions. "Triggering" is not, as we have seen, a known effect. Yet there seems to be some master plan at work. It may be — though this is but my own speculation — that the generation and radiation of heat within the earth has something to do with it. Certainly the heat engine we live on is a very steady machine, and one that we are measuring very rapidly. Lord Kelvin would have liked that!

VIII

Earthquake Oddities

Somehow the poor old earth blunders along.
— JAMES RUSSELL LOWELL

Do you knock on wood when you speak of your own good luck? Do you believe that a dream has some special meaning about your future? Or have you some uneasy feeling about the number thirteen? Well, we hope that you are not superstitious and do not believe in mystical powers or devilish interference in human affairs.

Sir Gerald and the forces of Nature

Somehow, however, one must explain the singular experience of Lieutenant Colonel Sir Gerald Lenox-Conyngham, of the Royal Engineers. The people of Montserrat, in the British West Indies, were troubled in 1938 by a lasting and ominous series of rumblings from the earth. They feared an earthquake or a volcanic outbreak. In desperation they appealed to the Colonial Office in London for advice or reassurance. That Office, believing in common with most Britishers that the Royal Society knew everything, turned to them for something to be done about Montserrat.

The Society saw fit to send a deputation to look into the matter — perhaps an explanation of the rumblings would help. Certainly no one, least of all any member of the Society, thought for a moment that anything could be done to stop Nature's rumblings.

Sir Gerald, lately returned from duty with the Geodetic Survey of India, was tall, commanding, and dignified. He was the very figure of the English gentleman and officer, the kind who could equally well command the obedience of Indian soldiers or the respect of his peers in the Royal Society. So he was selected to head the Royal Commission to Montserrat.

His arrival at the tiny island was doubtless most impressive. As he stepped ashore in his six feet and more of dignity, he must have seemed fully capable of assuming control, even of Nature's rumblings.

But the noises — they had stopped! There was no sound to be heard. Why was this — certainly the forces of Nature in the earth under Montserrat owed Sir Gerald no duty to obey. But now all was quiet. They all waited with mounting impatience.

"It's strange," they told Sir Gerald over and over again, "the rumblings were going on as you approached the harbor!"

He was never to know what it was all about, for nothing happened. So presently Sir Gerald returned home, the prestige of the Royal Society never having stood higher.

Earthquakes on schedule

If the experience of Sir Gerald seems a strange coincidence, then what of the earthquake at Seattle in April, 1950? It was a commonplace earthquake in every respect except its timing — scientists will never explain that!

There had been an extremely damaging earthquake throughout the Puget Sound area just one year before on April 13, 1949. Heavy damage had occurred at Olympia and Tacoma. At Seattle there was some damage, but only one death had occurred. According to the story, that was due to heart failure — a man who couldn't stand the excitement of seeing Seattle's famous Smith Tower sway during the shock!

The Seismological Society of America was in session at Seattle. The seismologists were well aware of the shock of the previous year, though none of them attached any importance to the date of the shock — the thirteenth of the month. Some Seattle people however, including news reporters, must have thought it ominous, for they asked the scientists whether Seattle would have another shock on the anniversary date.

Of course the scientists scoffed at such an idea. It was pure superstition, they told the newsmen, and their denials went duly to the papers for the reassurance of Seattle's people.

But Nature didn't believe the scientists! In her own time and for her own reasons she had her earthquake. Exactly one year, fifteen hours, and eight minutes after the Smith Tower danced in 1949, the people of Puget Sound felt the earth shaking again. True, it was gentle, but it was right on time! It was right on time to confound several embarrassed seismologists, who will never explain how it happened.

I have long been amazed at a prediction that came true — most unbelievably. It was by Omori, of Japan, who had been trying to work out a law of prediction based on the timing of past earthquakes. He found no law, to his sadness, but he made one of the few correct predictions in all history. After studying the many Pacific area earthquakes leading up to the San Francisco disaster of 1906, he made his prediction. In April of that year he announced where the next two great earthquakes should occur, one in the northern part of the Pacific belt, the other in the South American region of Peru and Chile. In August of that same year a strong earthquake shook each of the areas Omori had named. They happened on the very same day!

What tricks of Nature are these? Not being superstitious, we must believe that these things were pure coincidence, as they were, without doubt. But certainly such happenings leave lasting impressions in the minds of simple people, and profound wonder at the ways of an inscrutable Nature.

Broken boundaries and nonexistent rocks

Nature's earthquakes have more queer ways than just the matter of their timing. They often work the most annoying and expensive tricks on men. The consequences may be serious, as when one of southern California's many earthquakes dislodged the international boundary with Mexico where it crosses the hot plains of the Imperial Valley. I never knew how the two nations reconciled their broken boundary. Perhaps they just decided to let Nature have her way, and put up with the jog in the line.

No one can guess how many ships have been jolted by earthquake shocks coming upward through the water from somewhere deep below the sea. Ship-masters always suppose they have struck a sunken rock or reef. Chartmakers do not really believe such rocks exist in deep parts of the ocean, but they cannot safely overlook these reports as long as there is even the slightest possibility. Ocean charts are therefore much marked by sunken-rock symbols in the places where the jolting of ships has been experienced. Most, however, are marked "doubtful." It is quite a problem for chartmarkers, who do not like doubtful things in their work. However the ship reports are useful to seismologists in locating undersea earthquakes.

Sinking ground layers

More costly, though equally well hidden, were the effects of a mild earthquake in November, 1949, which centered some miles deep in the Los Angeles and Long Beach area of southern California. It was hardly felt, and no damage was done in the cities. People thought it of no consequence until they learned what had really happened. There are great oil fields in the vicinity, with wells reaching far down into the ground. The sand layers 1700 feet below the ground slipped a few inches — not far, but just enough to cut off two hundred producing oil wells and stop their flow. This unseen damage was very real, for it cost nearly fifty thousand dollars each to redrill all those wells.

Perhaps such an earthquake is caused when the oilmen draw their petroleum from the ground. Enough has flowed out through the wells to cause dangerous settlement of the land in parts of Long Beach and San Pedro. So has the pumping of ground water for the irrigation of the San Joaquin Valley some hundreds of miles to the north. However no one knows whether to expect resulting earthquakes in that vast farming land. To keep track of the changes in land level, the Coast and Geodetic Survey has run thousands of miles of precise level lines, and remeasured the heights of survey points throughout large areas.

Some other pranks

The experience of the Cathedral authorities of Christchurch, New Zealand, was less expensive but very frustrating. Eiby reports that earthquake shocks repeatedly knocked down the spire. Since well-regulated cathedrals must have spires, the authorities kept trying to keep one up where it should be. They tried everything they could think of, even inventing a special cross mounted on bearings so it could swing like a pendulum. This was knocked down in its turn, even after having been consecrated by a bishop hauled aloft in a bos'n's chair. The final solution of this ticklish problem lay in the building of a wooden spire, more resilient than metal, which has stood now for some years.

The Nevada earthquake of 1954 — the shock of magnitude 7.1 that left such tremendous scarp faulting on the side of Fairview Peak — broke the earth in a wall some fifteen or twenty feet high along the western side of Dixie Valley. At one place a flimsy prospector's shack stood entirely undamaged a few feet from that fearsome break in the earth. One can only suppose that in such a strong shock a great business building in a city would have collapsed completely.

That was the good fortune of an old wooden shack of no value. The Kern County shock of July, 1952, which was somewhat more violent, treated the towns of southern California to no such good fortune. The damage was tremendous, especially at Bakersfield. It was near there, on the route of the Southern Pacific Railway through the Tehachapi Mountains, that a three hundred foot distance between the portals of two tunnels was shortened by no less than eight feet! The tracks were squeezed into grotesque shapes, and one tunnel required major reconstruction.

The mystery of the disappearing rail

The S-curves of the warped tracks wove drunk-enly into the mouth of the tunnel. One of the rails was found afterward with several feet of its length buried inside the massive concrete wall of the tunnel. Its curving loop led directly into the wall, where it was completely lost to sight until, many feet farther along in the tunnel, it emerged and came to light again. Explaining this sort of Chinese puzzle wasn't easy. The engineers decided that the heavy wall itself must have lifted to make a wide crack into which the bending rail found its way, then

The Kern County, California, earthquake of 1952 left the Southern Pacific tracks in this strange condition in tunnel No. 3 in the Tehachapi Mountains!

Courtesy Pacific Fire Rating Bureau and Southern Pacific Railway

Train upset by the 1906 California earthquake.

fallen upon the rail so tightly that it looked as if it had been built that way!

Earthquake effects are often simply amusing. In 1958 the national news services radioed to the corners of the land the sad plight of a grocery store at Juneau which had ketchup and pickles all over the floor. In 1961 a small shock in Washington State made news when it knocked two glass pitchers off the shelves of Aunt Nellie's Antique Parlor at Portland, Oregon. We hope they weren't too valuable! But the same shock had a good effect too. It freed a door in a woman's apartment, that had been tightly stuck since a shock of the previous year. After this it worked perfectly.

Landslides and other effects on earth

It is not enough that man's works and his houses are smashed by Nature's whims. The earth herself is often torn apart when she has her earthquakes. The damage is not only in the rock layers of the crust — the very frame of the earth — but also in the soft masses of dirt and gravel and loose materials lying on the surface.

Unlike the crustal breaks, which are called *tectonic* because they affect the structure of the earth, these disturbances are *superficial* — that is, on the surface. But they are not always little. Sometimes they are the most dramatic and damaging of all earthquake effects.

When the newspapers print earthquake pictures of cracked highway pavements or landslides that block railway lines, or other such disturbances, you see these superficial effects. They are the settlement or slumping of earth masses jarred loose by the earth vibrations — jarred loose to change the look of Nature.

We recall that the California earthquake of 1906 sent a wet meadow slithering half a mile downhill. Persons who remember reading newspaper accounts

of the great earthquake of May 22, 1960, in Chile,
may recall that a twenty-five-mile stretch of high
ground in the mountainous Lake District was reported to have dropped a thousand feet! I think
we must interpret this to mean landslides along a
twenty-five-mile front.   Even that would be something to see — landslides for twenty-five miles!

Of course the material landed in heaps along the
foot of the mountain slope. It was not a gentle fall,
and certainly no one could have ridden safely down
on the falling materials. On the other hand the
earthquake of December 16, 1920, in Kansu, western China, made such a ride quite possible.

A quarter of a mile of country road slid sideways
a mile or so down the slope of a hillside so gently
that the roadside trees were not even disturbed.
Coming at last to rest after their unbelievable ride,
they stood as straight as ever in a line beside their
wandering stretch of road. There are good photographs, fortunately, to let us know this actually
happened.

The land formation that permitted this unusual
sideslip was *loess*. That is ground built up in long
centuries of time out of airborne dust from other
places, sometimes very far away. This sort of soil
is easily disturbed, although it has some remarkable
qualities, such as the ability to stand in vertical

The Kansu, China, earthquake of 1920 caused this quarter-mile stretch of country road to slide sideways nearly a mile downhill. The slide was so gentle that the trees beside the road stood throughout their unusual ride!

bluffs. We have loess formations in our country. One example is the hills surrounding Vicksburg, on the bank of the Mississippi River.

Loose earth and gravel sliding into river beds blocks the flow of water, and creates temporary lakes and great flood danger. This happened in the Himalayan earthquake of 1950. The same kind of distress followed the 1960 disaster in Chile. In 1959, a vast landslide blocked the valley of the

Madison River in Montana, during an earthquake in August of that year.

The birth of Quake Lake

In the scenic river gorge a short distance below Hebgen Lake, where tourists camped in great numbers, an entire half of a mountain collapsed and fell roaring into the river bed. Some campers were lost, but the more widespread effects were yet to come. The waters of the Madison found the way completely stopped. A new lake was born, soon christened "Quake Lake." The water rose all too fast toward the top of Nature's dam, 130 feet above the old river bed.

Something had to be done. If the lake were to overflow the dam it would start scouring away the mass of loose earth, rock, and mud. It is Nature's way for this to happen fast enough to release the water of the new lake almost all at once. There would be a disastrous rush of water, and violent flooding through the downstream valley of the river. A few miles below the dam the river ran through settled valleys, with farms and towns. They must be saved.

Public works engineers were on the scene almost at once, coming by light plane and helicopter, to see what could be done. It became clear soon enough what their task was to be. They must create a spill-way across the top of that piled-up mass of material, and get it paved before the water rose to flow through it. This would save the towns of Varney and Ennis and McAllister. Perhaps even Three Forks itself, some eighty miles downstream from the menacing Quake Lake, was in danger.

It was done, thanks to the skill and daring of determined construction workers. The bulldozers and

There was little left of this road along the shore of Hebgen Lake, Montana, after the earthquake of 1959.

trucks and other heavy machinery got there somehow over roads never meant for such loads, over
roads washed out and collapsed, and over no roads
at all. Working desperately on unstable and treach-
erous piles of earth and rock, they finally cleared a
way over the pile. They removed the worst of the
boulders, scooped out a channel, and got it paved.

When Quake Lake filled up to meet the new spill-
way, the water began flowing smoothly, and the
dried-up bed of the Madison came alive again. It
was a relief to have the danger removed, so the
valley settlers were safe again. But lives were lost
in the slide, and the beautiful scenery was sunken,
perhaps forever, below the new lake.

Submarine rivers

The Grand Banks earthquake of 1929 did even
greater violence, but this was far from sight under
the North Atlantic Ocean. The shock itself was
great enough to sway tall buildings in New England
and to be felt by people in New York. Great waves
entered the bays of nearby Newfoundland. But the
most unusual result was the snapping of a number
of transatlantic cable lines. These heavily armored
telegraph wires on the bed of the ocean were broken, one after the other. The exact moment when

the messages stopped coming through was known for each cable.

Immediately a question became apparent. Why did the breaks occur at different times? Why not all together at the time of the earthquake? Some, in fact, were an hour or more later than others. Why this delayed reaction?

Maurice Ewing and Bruce Heezen of Columbia University, studied long, then gave the answer. The shock of the earthquake jolted the water-soaked mud layers perched on the edges of the Grand Banks. Loosened masses of material started to slide down along the gullies leading off toward deep water. Stirred-up silt swirled in the nearby water, making it muddy and heavy with dirt. Because of its weight it also started to run down the slopes with the rivulets of mud. Soon these little streams joined into rivers under the sea.

They grew bigger and faster as they spilled down toward the ocean depths. They scoured out more of the bottom until they carried tremendous quantities of mud. As they gained speed they picked up heavier dirt — even pebbles and rocks. By the time this raging mass reached the bottom of the Atlantic there was force enough to snap the first of the cables like a motor truck running through a stretched thread.

Later, and farther down under thousands of feet of water, there was another cable. Then another. Finally, scores of miles from the source of all this, there waited the last cable to be snapped. Ocean scientists have found the gravel from those submarine rivers scattered hundreds of miles out over the abyssal depths of the Atlantic, where the waters finally slowed and dropped their unusual cargo.

When the scientists made the necessary computations based on the timing of the cable breaks and the distances involved, and announced the speed of the submarine rivers, many refused to believe. It must have been as high as fifty miles an hour. That is perhaps ten times the speed of the rivers we see flowing above ground. But Ewing and Heezen have showed that the necessary energy was there, and that such speeds must have existed, at least briefly, in 1929.

Cracks in the earth

The birth of new islands, grown out of the sea in earthquakes, is an oft-heard tale. The Roman philosopher and historian Seneca recorded the birth of new islands in the Aegean Sea hundreds of years before, but there seems to be no way to verify his story. It may be the merest myth. We have read of the new island in Sponge Bay, after an earthquake of 1931 in New Zealand. This is known to be an actual case, though new islands are in most cases the results of volcanoes rather than earthquakes.

In May, 1960, news dispatches from Chile spoke of trees being sucked into the earth. I think we may take that story with a grain of salt, although it is possible that cracks in the topsoil opened wide enough to permit the trees to fall in. Stories of people having been swallowed in cracks during earthquakes are common, and some of them are true, despite widespread scepticism.

One story told by Eiby can be read with amusement if not belief. It relates how the bed of the Waiau River in New Zealand opened and sucked in great quantities of water, then closed with force enough to spout the water three hundred feet high. That is ridiculous, of course, but there is no doubt about occasional great and unusual pressures in the earth. In Japan old buried wharf pilings, long out of sight underground, popped out like seeds from a squeezed orange when pressure waves from an earthquake passed by.

There are people to whom the whole subject of earthquakes and their effects is a great joke. I have known jokesters to greet a seismologist with the quip, "Had a *bumper* crop this year, old man?" I recall also that California chambers of commerce took the matter of earthquakes very lightly in the days before the San Francisco shock.

The Californians then wanted tourists and settlers. They worked hard to still any earthquake fears. One imaginative writer even described an earthquake as a "celestial" or heavenly experience. He must never have felt a really strong one.

Even if an earthquake were a celestial event, Hal Engle wouldn't want one. He is a California engineer who has analyzed earthquake effects for insurance companies during many years. He was on a water tower examining the damage done by the Kern County earthquake a few years ago, when a strong aftershock shook the tower most ominously. It clanked and shivered, and Hal squeezed the steel almost hard enough to leave his fingerprints engraved in the metal. Finally, safe on the ground, he breathed deeply in relief, and said:

"I didn't feel celestial at all. In fact I had a great desire to become a bird and fly away!"

IX

Earthquakes Under the Sea

. . . Blow wind, swell billow, and swim bark!
The storm is up, and all is on the hazard.
— SHAKESPEARE

It was April Fool's Day, 1946. A day for jokes? Perhaps a day for very wry jokes indeed!

At Unimak Pass, the point where the Alaskan mainland ends and the long chain of the Aleutian Islands begins its nine-hundred-mile sweep to the west, the Scotch Cap Lighthouse stood shining in the night to guide ships through the rough waters and strong currents from the Pacific Ocean into the Bering Sea.

The light shone from the tower of a heavy concrete blockhouse on a rocky ledge thirty feet above the waters of Unimak. It was nearly new, and as strong as it could be.

Soon after two in the morning of that April Fool's Day the sea leaped suddenly upward at Scotch Cap Lighthouse, driven by some mischievous force. The building was engulfed. In a moment it was crushed. With a grinding of broken masonry it disappeared in the sweep of the water.

Five men living there to attend the light must never have known what struck them. The Coast Guard sent planes when they failed to answer radio calls after daylight, and the world soon knew. The airwaves buzzed with reports of enormous waves dashing about the North Pacific Ocean. Planes and ships began searching, but they could find no waves.

In 1946 most seismologists recorded earthquakes by focusing pinpoints of light on photographic paper sheets, which were developed to show the wiggles of the light dancing to an earthquake wave. As American seismologists went about the development of their records that morning, they soon noticed the strong marks of a new earthquake. The radio news had said nothing of a bad shock anywhere, but earthquakes are quite common, and many do no damage. Probably it was under the sea.

The seismologists, always eager to know where large earthquakes are, began exchanging readings. The first to plot the position were not surprised. It lay under two miles of water in an ocean trench

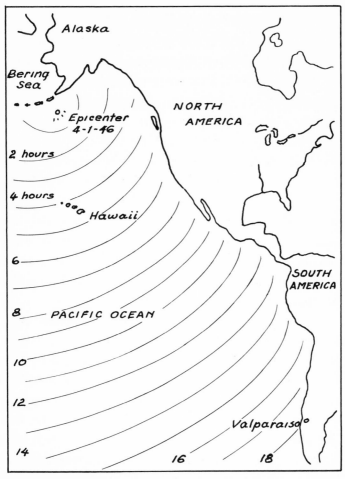

Map showing the progress of the great tsunami of April, 1946, over the eastern Pacific. The lines show the positions of the wave front at hourly intervals following the earthquake near Alaska. It took eighteen hours to reach Chile, eight thousand miles away, traveling sometimes six hundred miles an hour. It reached Valparaiso with a height of five feet.

known to be a breeder of such shocks. It was
eighty miles southeast of Alaska's Scotch Cap Lighthouse.

The wave reaches Hawaii

Lieutenant Commander Patterson, the Government seismologist at Honolulu, was breakfasting
that morning on the *lanai* (verandah) of his beach
house. He thought of his good fortune to be in
Hawaii where the weather is always good and the
rustle of the palms and the fragrance of the flowers
seemed never-ending. He must hurry. It was near
time for his morning visit to the seismograph station
to develop the past day's record.

Patterson glanced toward the sea for a last look
at the sparkling waters he loved so much. He
couldn't believe his eyes — the water was gone, and
the sea bottom lay bare and ugly as far as he could
see! Amazed, he started down to see this thing,
when a line of high white breakers loomed in the
distance. A wall of water was coming fast! He
barely got back ahead of it. With a bang it hit the
beach, then the house.

The next few moments were a wild struggle to put
his valuables on shelves above the water, and to
keep his furniture from floating away. When the
flood had gone his house was a shambles. But he

Courtesy Corps of Engineers, U. S. Army

The most dramatic picture ever made of an approaching seismic sea wave. The great mass of water has just started to collapse a warehouse. The man pointed out by the arrow was killed seconds after the picture was made. Taken from the deck of a ship moored alongside, Hilo, Hawaii, 1946.

was lucky. Some nearby houses had floated away or collapsed completely.

This happened in many places about the shores of the beautiful islands. Beach roads and bridges were undermined, and houses were washed away, to make a staggering total of losses. Some places had it much worse than others.

People at Hilo, on the "Big Island" of Hawaii, didn't notice the first gentle rise of the water in their harbor. All was peaceful — what could happen there? They didn't know, nor probably care, that four and a half hours before in the Gulf of Alaska, 2375 miles to the north, an earth shock had made the sea bottom jump. But some of them noticed when the water ran out of the harbor, leaving ugly mud flats and reefs they had never seen before. It was a sudden surprise and delight to small children, who ran out to see the flopping fish and the strange sea animals.

If these excited children saw the big wave coming, they certainly had no time to get away. It roared past them, splintering wharves and breaking concrete walls on the shore. Then it crashed into the city itself. In a few moments the whole business section of Hilo lay in ruins. It was a sprawling litter of what had been railroad cars, automobiles and trucks, buildings, and boats. As the water ran back it floated away whole houses, jumbled wreckage, and three-quarters of a million dollars' worth of sugar.

That giant breaker and the ones that followed during hours of terror destroyed twenty-five million dollars' worth of property. It was the worst wave disaster in Hawaii's history. It was a wry April Fool's Day joke!

The surviving men of Hilo went about the work of cleaning up the wreckage in which 173 of their relatives and friends had died. They asked sadly

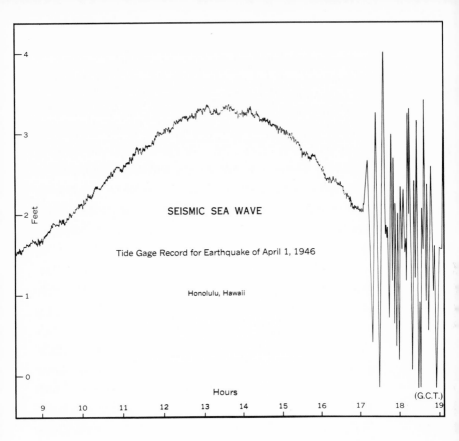

SEISMIC SEA WAVE

Tide Gage Record for Earthquake of April 1, 1946

Honolulu, Hawaii

Hours

(G.C.T.)

The great waves and sudden change of sea level caused by the tsunami of 1946 are shown on this tide gage record made at Honolulu. The long curve shows the tide; the small jiggles show the ordinary waves; and the violent ups and downs at the right show the arriving sea wave.

why someone hadn't warned them of that terrible wave born of a submarine earthquake.

The famous volcano scientist T. A. Jagger had long been a student of the Kilauea crater on Hawaii

Island near Hilo. Years before he had tried to warn them. He had a seismograph, and had sometimes known in time of distant undersea earthquakes, but he never knew whether a sea wave would come or not. The people paid little attention to his uncertain warnings. Hilo must await the advantages of modern electronics and a system of cooperating stations to have a reliable warning. Even that might not be enough, for people easily forget when things don't happen very often. It wasn't enough in 1960, when Hilo was struck again, and many died in spite of warnings.

The Japanese call a seismic sea wave a *tsunami.* Scientists like the word because its meaning is exact and certain. The tsunami, like other kinds of flooding from the sea, is often called a "tidal wave," but this is wrong. It has nothing at all to do with the tide.

One kind of high water wrongly called a tidal wave often floods the coast when there is a storm at sea. High winds drive the water before them, making it pile high against the coast. The water also rises in the central part of the storm because the air pressure is low. Tropical hurricanes have centers of extremely low air pressure surrounded by whirling winds. Such a storm caused the disastrous flood at

Galveston, Texas, in 1900, when five thousand lives were lost. A great seawall has since been built to protect the city. Another hurricane strayed far north to New England in 1938, driving and lifting the sea water to heights thirty or forty feet above normal. Large areas were damaged on the coast of Long Island and in the mouth of the Connecticut River. But these were not true tsunamis.

Perhaps one true tsunami big enough to do damage strikes somewhere on earth each year. N. H. Heck, in his list of historic and well-proven tsunamis, has 270 cases, mostly within the past two hundred years. Heck's earliest tsunami was at Potidaea, Greece, in 479 B.C. Others have visited many parts of the world. Japan, Chile, and Greece have been hit time after time. In 1724, twenty-four ships were destroyed at Callao, Peru, by an eighty-foot wave. Japan had thirty thousand killed in 1293, and so did Italy in 1783.

Great tsunamis

Perhaps the best-known great tsunami started from a submarine earthquake 150 miles off the shores of Japan on June 15, 1896. The Japanese gave it the name Sanriku, since it struck three provinces, and in the Japanese language "san" means three and "riku" stands for land. It was in the early evening, and the people were enjoying the pleasant weather by the shores. They hardly noticed a small preliminary wave disturbance, and were unprepared for the great wave, reported to be 93 feet high, that suddenly dashed over them. From this wave we have the sad record of 27,122 deaths and 10,617 houses washed away.

Probably the most spectacular seismic sea wave reliably reported, and certainly one of the greatest on record, struck the coast of Kamchatka at Cape Lopatka in 1737 with a height of two hundred and ten feet! Fortunately there were not many people there at the time.

The explosion of Krakatoa volcano in the East Indies in 1883 sent walls of water racing through the Sunda Strait to kill 36,500 helpless people on the shores of Java and Sumatra. This, however, was not a true seismic sea wave, since it was not an earthquake that caused it.

The tsunami that helped to make the famous Lisbon earthquake so disastrous was only seven feet high at the city itself, but it was said to have reached a height of thirty feet farther south on the opposite shore of the river. A wave so high that it went over the tops of palm trees was reported to have struck places on the shores of Hawaii in 1868. Others have broken seawalls and tossed large blocks of masonry about like pebbles. At the port of Corral, Chile, the wave of 1960 washed an eleven-thousand-ton ship from the harbor completely over the town and out to sea. The U.S. Gunboat *Wateree* was lost in 1868 by being swept a quarter-mile inland near Arica, on the coast of Chile in South America, by a wave estimated to be seventy feet high.

Now what is known about these tsunamis? Little was known in the past, certainly, beyond the obvious fact that they occurred after earthquakes. Even this was not too certain until modern times because many undersea earthquakes passed unnoticed in the four-fifths of the earth covered by oceans. Moreover, only a few of the many undersea earthquakes do cause tsunamis. That was the trouble with Jaggar's "predictions" at Hawaii — he didn't know how to tell which earthquakes to be afraid of.

How a tsunami begins

Until recently many scientists believed that submarine landslides and currents or rivers of heavy silt-laden water must be the cause. For instance, the fast undersea streams from the Grand Banks earthquake might seem to have had energy enough to start such waves. Although the energy was great, it was probably not enough. Besides, it is not clear how the energy could be transformed into waves. A better answer was needed.

We know enough about the fault zones under the sea to be sure that some of them produce vertical movements of the earth's crust. Sudden rising of a large area of the ocean bottom will lift the water out of its usual level. The work done by the earth's crust in lifting so much water is very great. The water has much energy to use up in sinking back to its former place. A corresponding result would follow sinking instead of rising of the sea floor.

Like the ripples that spread outward from a water disturbance in a pool, we see the settlement of the displaced water sending surface waves over an entire ocean. But what a difference there is from the ripples! Here there are billions of tons of water out of place. The "ripples" are truly gigantic.

They are started ten minutes or more apart, because of the time it takes such a large mass of water to readjust itself. They depart at jet-plane speed. In the deeper parts of the Pacific it may be nearly six hundred miles an hour. Waves going out at such speeds, and so many minutes apart, become widely separated. In fact the crests are sometimes a hundred miles or more apart. So each wave is a bulge a few feet high, probably no higher than the ground uplift that started it, and many scores of miles long. Ships at sea and aircraft overhead cannot see all of such a bulge, so they never know when a tsunami is passing them. It is as much invisible to them as the tide itself.

In some respects the tsunami acts like the tidal wave. Both are long swellings of the water surface speeding unseen across the ocean. The tide, like tsunamis, was long misunderstood. The ancient Chinese, typically mystical and imaginative in their approach to unknown things, thought the ocean water was the earth's blood, and the tide was the beating of its pulse! They called it the breathing of the earth. Now that we recognize it as a wave, we may compare the tsunami to it.

Both have dramatic effects. The Yangtze River in China and the Petitcodiac in eastern Canada have unusually high tides. Large quantities of water have to enter. This is held back by the force of the river current, until a wave builds up. This dashes upstream in a foaming wall of water called a *bore.* Tourists come from afar to witness the tidal bore in the Petitcodiac. The tsunami sometimes builds up a wall of water similar to the bore when it approaches a coastline, although the reasons are somewhat different.

How far does it reach?

The speed of the wave across the ocean depends on the water depth. We can predict how long it will take to arrive at a distant place, if only we know the depths everywhere. But we don't. There are large areas of very poorly surveyed ocean. Yet it is still possible to predict travel times with fair accuracy. All the tsunamis reaching Hawaii since the time of the Hilo disaster have been predicted within a very few minutes. If one arrives a little ahead of the predicted time, oceanographers simply say that the wave found deeper waters and a better path than they knew about!

The enormous energy of the tsunamis sends them very long distances. The one from Unimak Pass in 1946, which hit Scotch Cap and Hilo so hard, reached Valparaiso, Chile, in eighteen hours, after traveling more than eight thousand miles. It arrived with a height of five feet, and was followed by smaller waves that took many hours to die down.

An earthquake near Valparaiso in 1906 sent a twelve-foot tsunami into the Bay of Maalaea, in Hawaii, where it broke the chain of an anchored ship.

Hours later it reached Japan, almost eleven thousand miles away, where it did further damage. An earlier one born near Iquique, also in Chile, sent an eight-foot wave to Hakodate, Japan, killing thousands in the Fiji Islands along the way.

A tsunami, like the tide, oscillates, or pulsates, within the confines of an ocean. It is sometimes reflected from coast lines. At Hanasaki, Japan, there were waves from the 1946 Alaska earthquake that must have been reflected from the North American coast. Waves arriving late at Honolulu had been reflected from the submerged sea-bottom slopes near Asia. It has been said that a tsunami might reflect back and forth between the Pacific shores for as long as a week.

The growing wave

Since the tsunami is but a few feet high while crossing the ocean, it may be asked why it grows to such frightful heights when it nears land. This is because of its tremendous energy, which lies in the speed and height of the wave. It is the way of such long waves that their speed is high in deep water, and slower in shallow places. Nearing a coast the wave must slow down. The energy goes then to make greater height. It cannot all be lost at once. The wave grows higher and higher. It is also, in a sense, "tripped" by the shallow sea, holding back the bottom of the wave and making it somewhat like a wall of water.

The same effect is seen when the gentle ground swell of the sea — mild enough in appearance — approaches a bathing beach. It grows higher until it becomes a breaker. Then it crashes on the sand with the force that makes bathing exciting — if not indeed impossible. Those who have ridden surfboards on the crests of breakers on Hawaiian beaches can appreciate this.

The reaction of the tsunami on a shoaling coastline has been described by Walter Munk, of the Scripps Institution of Oceanography in California. It is an "organ-pipe" effect. Just as the pipe amplifies the music until it swells and echoes through the spaces of a great cathedral, so does the confining shape of the shallow coast amplify the tsunami wave until it rises to great and damaging heights.

We must consider also how the water tends to pulsate in a bay. In a confined basin there is a natural period of pulsation. It depends of the size and shape of the place. The effect, known as the *seiche*, is troublesome to scientists studying the motions of the tide, for it adds extra wave effects that complicate their study. It adds extra wave effects, sometimes of great size, in bays like that of Hilo, where tsunamis do their harm. The seiche can be started by winds, tides, or the tsunami itself. Those who would try to guess the danger from waves must understand the seiche effects.

Tsunamis show their worst behavior in certain places, and Hilo must be one of them. The shapes of the offshore sea bottom and the coast are bad for Hilo. And Hilo Harbor is a confined basin with a natural pulsation that is strongly triggered by tsunami waves. The water "resonates" like the air in the organ pipe, and slops higher and higher. Remember how the coffee in a cup often slops over at the slightest jogging of the cup.

Engineers are working hard to find a design of breakwater and seawalls that may control and change the seiche period of Hilo Harbor enough to fend off the attacks of future tsunamis. With time and enough money, they will succeed.

How to be forewarned

The people of Hilo asked after the 1946 tragedy why someone didn't warn them. The Coast and Geodetic Survey, and Patterson particularly, were criticized angrily for not issuing warnings of the tsunami. Everyone knew it came from an earthquake. The Survey maintained a seismograph station in Honolulu. They said anyone could put these two facts together and see that Patterson had failed! And this shows how little understanding people show when they are angry. Two facts put together do not necessarily make the truth.

It took a great deal of effort by Patterson to make them see that the recordings were on photographic paper that wasn't developed until eight o'clock in the morning. And there was no way to collect the necessary information so quickly from other stations thousands of miles away. Besides, no one knew any more than old Jaggar had known whether any particular earthquake would send a tsunami.

The need was very great, so the Government men went to work. First of all, new electronic instruments had to be invented, so the seismologists could see at any time by an ink-writing recorder what was going on. They had to be connected to electric-eye signals that would flash lights or ring bells when an earthquake wave was recorded at the station. Even in the middle of the night the seismologist would be called to do something about it.

Seismograph stations in Fairbanks and Sitka in Alaska, and at Tucson, Arizona, were fitted with the new instruments, and several stations run by California universities promised to help. Then a radio communications system was organized, with top priorities for earthquake messages. The tide station operators of the Coast and Geodetic Survey were instructed to watch for unusual waves, so they could report whether or not a tsunami came into being after any particular undersea earthquake. Things were getting ready by 1948.

From time to time there were submarine earthquakes in the Pacific. The seismologists all answered the bells and read their records quickly. Then they notified the central station at Honolulu, which was specially prepared for this duty. Patterson wasn't there, but others had taken his place. They took it very seriously, for they wanted to make no mistakes about it. The people were depending on them to make no mistakes. One of the Honolulu workers was heard to say, only half jokingly, that he and his fellows had not wished to fail and be the first Government men to be lynched in Hawaii!

When an earthquake had been plotted, messages went to the tide stations nearest the disturbance asking whether a tsunami had been registered on the gages. When one was found, its arrival time at Hawaii was estimated by using travel-time charts made by Coast and Geodetic Survey oceanographers. This was not too easy, for the speed depended on ocean depths which were not well known everywhere. However, they had done the best they could. In the end the travel-time charts worked very well.

On a number of occasions through the years tsunamis were predicted by the working of this system. Warnings were given to the military and civil authorities throughout the Islands. It was then their job to take care of warning the people. Some of the tsunamis did damage, but no one was killed by the raging waves. Other tsunamis were too small to be noticed. Since they always came within a few minutes of the predicted time, it was clear that the charts were satisfactory. Then came the great earthquake under the sea near Valdivia, Chile, on May 22, 1960.

Like so many others, that earthquake off the coast of Chile started tsunamis on paths of destruction. Waterfront areas in Chile fell before twenty-four foot waves, spawned when the faults broke and threw the sea bottom up in convulsive jerks. The waves killed hundreds before they raced away westward across the Pacific.

The warning system went immediately into operation. The stations answered the alarms, read their records, and sent fast messages to Honolulu. The radio news services told of the destructive waves in Chile — no check by tide stations was needed. The authorities received the warnings from the Government men and took all the action they could. Sirens screamed in the coastal towns. The radio blared. Police patrolled Hilo streets, warning the people to leave the city. The wave was predicted for midnight. It semed that all was ready.

Jerry Eaton, of the Geological Survey's Volcano Observatory at Kilauea, Jaggar's old station, and others from the observatory and from the Hawaii National Park, have told in the Bulletin of the Seismological Society of America what happened at Hilo. It is a graphic tale. After discussing their plans with the police they drove through blocked-off and deserted waterfront streets to a vantage point on the north end of the Wailuku bridge where they would have an excellent view. A short sprint along the highway would bring them to safety on high ground!

Just after midnight the water rose about four feet. Then it fell to a level three feet below normal. Then up it came again, this time overflowing the waterfront street, and then far down once again. Rocks always before covered came into sight, and a strange calm prevailed. Just after one o'clock the third and biggest wave approached. In the words of the report:

"At first there was only the sound, a dull rumble

like a distant train that came from the darkness . . .
all could hear the loudening roar as it came closer
. . . As our eyes searched . . . a pale wall of tumbling water, the broken crest of the third wave, was
caught in the dim light. . .

"At 1:04 A.M. the 20-foot-high nearly vertical
front of the in-rushing bore churned past our look-
out and we ran a few hundred feet toward safer
ground. Turning around, we saw a flood of water
pouring up the estuary. The top of the in-coming
current caught in the steel-grid roadway of the
south half of the bridge and sent a spray of water
high into the air. Seconds later, brilliant blue-white
electrical flashes . . . signalled that the wave had
crossed the sea wall and buffer zone and was washing the town with crushing force . . . Dull grating
sounds from buildings ground together by the waves
and sharp reports from snapped-off power poles
emerged from the flooded city now left in darkness
. . . the wave reached the power plant . . . and
after a brief greenish electrical arc that lit up the
sky above the plant, Hilo and most of the Island of
Hawaii were plunged into darkness."

Hilo had been stricken again! But this time there
had been many hours of warning. Yet sixty-one
heedless persons lost their lives! Some had gone at
first to the hills, and then tired of waiting and gone

back. They had said there had been other warnings when nothing happened. They couldn't be bothered. Others had stayed in town to see the excitement. Now their bodies lay crushed in the wreckage.

What was wrong? Obviously there had been a failure of public education. People didn't seem to realize that tsunamis, large or small, must be taken seriously. Something more was needed. Public education — yes! But also more information so the people would know when real danger threatened. The most common complaint was that no one had said with certainty that this would be another big one.

Tsunamis — still a mystery

The trouble was that no one knew how to tell. The warning system was reliable enough as to the actual birth of the tsunami and the time it would strike. But it could not say how big it would be when it got there. Reports of moderate waves at other Pacific islands on the way meant little because every locality has its own effect on the height of the wave.

Today there is a vigorous research study going on to find out how to predict the tsunami effects. It is a difficult problem. No one knows how high the wave generated by any particular earthquake will be. We must learn how to tell how much lift of the sea bottom it takes. We should know how high the tsunami is while it travels the ocean, and what the tide gage readings at outpost islands mean. We must appraise the conditions that govern what it will do when it reaches Hilo, or anywhere else. The problem is loaded with difficult questions and unknown answers.

The Government is working on the problem. So is the Geophysical Institute at the University of Hawaii, and so are oceanographic institutions in California and elsewhere. Private research laboratories and professors in universities have undertaken to find some of the answers. They all hope that the day will come when the seismologist can read his record, then say with confidence what sea-bottom disturbance occurred, what size of tsunami must have been caused, and what it will do when it arrives at any particular place.

The people of Hilo hope so, too. No one can hope to know when the next tsunami will be born. But when it is, the Honolulu men of the warning system will know the hour when it will strike. They hope the new research will help them to tell the people how much to expect.

X

The Earthquake and the Bay

The awful shadow of some unseen Power
Floats though unseen among us.
— SHELLEY

"A crazy nightmare exploded over the land!" That was the way one person described the great earthquake of July 9, 1958. It was late evening in the high country of the Fairweather Mountains of southeast Alaska. The earthquake was one more of an ages-long series characteristic of this region, where the land is rising and the mountains growing several feet higher in each century.

It was America's fourth-greatest earthquake, and one of its remarkable effects will perhaps never be equaled. For it was not only an earthquake and a shaking of the ground. It also triggered the most

199

appalling landslides and created the highest salt
water wave known to oceanographers.

These effects happened in Lituya Bay, the only
sheltered anchorage in a long and forbidding stretch
of the Alaskan coast between Cape Spencer and
Yakutat Bay. The rough seas of this part of the
Pacific and the rocky dangers of the coast made
Lituya Bay very attractive to fishermen, many of
whom came in to anchor for a night of rest. This
they did in spite of the bay's bad reputation for
dangers and violence that seemed very unlike its
usual quiet beauty.

From the coast Lituya leads inward seven miles
between rolling hills clad in richly dark evergreen
trees, to its head close by the foot of the high Fairweathers themselves. In the summertime Lituya's
banks abound with wild strawberries. In the water
float hundreds of little glistening icebergs suitable
for the mariners' iceboxes. In the center of the bay
a green forested island peeps forth from the dark
water.

To understand what happened in Lituya Bay, one
must know its peculiar shape. Its inner end leads
between two sentinel-like mountains into an inner
basin shaped like a cross-arm. At the south end
of this fjord towers the vertical face of Crillon
Glacier. At the north end is Lituya Glacier — one

Lituya Bay, Alaska, and the Fairweather Mountains, after the great earthquake and wave of 1958, showing the scoured shores and the place on Cenotaph Island where the wave went over.

of the villains in the story of Lituya's violence. Chunks of ice now and then fall into the water with splashes that resound among the cliffs. Normally there is profound quiet, broken only by a gull's occasional cry and the lapping of the waters against the rocky shores. The high Fairweathers, their snowy summits fifteen thousand feet in the eastern sky, form a breathtaking panorama. In this natural amphitheater an occasional boatman finds the quiet and majesty of a great cathedral.

Lituya Bay was discovered in 1786 by a Frenchman, Jean François de Galaup, Count de la Pérouse, in the course of a voyage of discovery. He anchored his two ships in great relief after a perilous passage through the entrance. A spit of land which he called La Chaussée, because it looked like a causeway, lies across the seaward end of the bay, leaving only a narrow channel between dangerous rocks. Through this the water races with each turn of the tide, altogether too fast and turbulent for safe navigation, so that mariners now use it only during the slack water period between the tides.

The waves of Lituya

But Perouse didn't know all this. His two ships were sucked in on the flooding tide, and they whirled past the rocks completely out of control. He later wrote in his diary that he had never seen two ships so near destruction.

Safe in the bay at last, he sent out sailors in boats to make a chart. Among other things Perouse's chart showed two Indian villages on the shore where none exist today. There is an Indian legend, which has not been confirmed, about the loss of the villages in a great wave, some men of the community having escaped by being at sea hunting sea otters in their canoes.

Perouse was saddened when two boatloads of his men were lost by being caught and capsized in the furiously ebbing water of the entrance channel. He erected a monument to their memory at the summit of the little island. It is now known by the name Cenotaph.

In 1935 Jim Huscroft, a fisherman, and a companion lived on the island while they salted down their salmon catch in casks. They had a cabin among trees fifty feet above the water. One day a sudden wave came down the bay toward them with the noise of a whole fleet of low-flying airplanes. They clambered to the top of their island and escaped, but the wave took their entire season's catch. In discouragement they left, and poor Jim died some years later in Juneau. Since then no one has lived in Lituya Bay, but the old cabin was destined to stand another twenty-two years awaiting an end in the higher wave of 1958.

Even though uninhabited, Lituya has always attracted attention. Some years ago Dr. Don Miller, of the United States Geological Survey, noticed an unusual condition of the trees on the hillsides about the bay. Everywhere below a certain line they were all young, as he could tell by counting the tree rings.

All these trees had sprung up since 1936, the year of Huscroft's wave. Higher up they were much older. So Miller reasoned that a great wave — Huscroft's, of course — had scoured the lower area clean. All the trees had been removed at that time, he said.

Searching further he found another line separating trees of a hundred years' age from still older ones higher up. Miller recalled the Indian legend of an early great wave, and the old chart showing the Indian villages, and he felt sure that he now knew when they had disappeared. It must have been in the winter of 1853–1854, according to the tree-ring count.

Miller called the lines of separation trimlines. He traced the lines along the hillsides, finding in amazement that they reached hundreds of feet above the bay in some places. He wrote a scientific paper about it, and presented it at a meeting of the Geological Society of America, but when the members heard Miller speak of wave heights of hundreds of feet many disbelieved him, and for a long time Miller's trimlines were in doubt. But Miller was not deterred. He continued his investigations, later discovering evidence of still other trimlines. Now it is believed that there have been at least four great waves in Lituya Bay in the past hundred years.

Human memory is short. Although the fishermen know about the perils of Lituya's entrance channel, where they skirt hidden rocks every time they enter, the old tales of great waves have been easily forgotten. After all, they don't happen very often. So the fishermen continue using Lituya as a haven.

July 9, 1958

There were three boats anchored in Lituya Bay the evening of July 9. The occupants were asleep, and like everyone else in southeast Alaska that night, they were quite unaware of the overstressed rocks ten miles deep under the towering mountains to the east.

So were ten Canadian mountaineers who had just returned from climbing Mount Fairweather, on the boundary of Alaska and Canada, where it stands as British Columbia's highest point. They had first planned to spend the night on Lituya's shore, but had flown to Juneau two hours before because their pilot was worried about the weather. It was the luckiest thing that could have happened to them, but not because of the weather. That stayed good!

A few miles south on the shore of Lake Crillon were sixteen men under geologist Virgil Mann, preparing to change their camp early next morning to Cenotaph Island, where they would use Huscroft's old cabin. Three persons from Yakutat, a hundred miles north of Lituya, were picking strawberries on Khantaak Island, in Yakutat Bay. This was not far from where the strong earthquake of 1899 had caused the land to rise nearly fifty feet in one leap out of the sea. But that was far from their thoughts. They were intent on getting home with their pails of fresh red berries. It would soon be dark.

This was the moment Nature chose for the rocks under the Fairweathers to break and relieve their stress. The stored-up power, like that in a stretched rubber band when it breaks, was released violently.

Then the earthquake

The peaks of the Fairweathers shivered amid plumes of flying snow as great avalanches began their descent toward Lituya Bay. A hundred and fifty miles of mountain uplands and glacier valleys danced as the waves raced through the ground. The coastal lowlands shivered as twenty-foot geysers gushed from the ground, building sandhills as they spouted. Great cracks opened up, one of them big enough to swallow a truck where it stood by a cabin on the Akwe River north of Lituya.

The land where the strawberry pickers stood awaiting their boat seemed to leap twenty feet in the air, then collapse into a mad jumble of swirling waters. Where they had stood, there now flowed back and forth with tides some ninety feet of water — enough twice over to float the world's greatest ships.

Public alarm and damage occurred over an area of four hundred thousand square miles — nearly the size of Texas and California combined — reaching such places as Anchorage, Cordova, and Ketchikan. Submarine cables were broken by sea-bottom disturbances in places as far as two hundred and fifty miles away. The airport runway at Yakutat was cracked, and eleven hundred helium cylinders stacked nearby in neat rows all fell over toward the south, as if bowing to the source of all the trouble. At Lake Crillon, near the geologists' camp, whole stands of young fir trees had fifteen feet of their tops broken off, which fell in unison toward the southwest.

A hundred and twenty miles east at Juneau a chimney toppled, bells rang to the swaying of the ground, and a sandbar shook like jelly. Goods fell from store shelves, and the audience in Juneau's Capitol Theater was so alarmed that they had to be quieted by the stern commands of the manager. At Seattle, a near-record thousand miles away, the Coast and Geodetic Survey measured more than an inch of back-and-forth motion of the ground. The musicians in a concert shell floating on the waters of Seattle's Lake Union felt themselves swaying for minutes. Certainly that shell was one of the largest seismometers on record.

Even at sea the effects were frightening. One man fishing several miles offshore said afterward that he had felt himself to be riding on a big explosion. Another thought his boat had jumped twelve feet high. A woman's voice came over the radio asking frantically how much their boat could stand. Some miles south of Lituya at Point Astrolabe a whole mountain was reported falling into the sea.

Of more lasting concern was the later difficulty of salmon seining through masses of dead halibut and octopuses, drifting among uncounted stripped and barkless logs, masses of ice, and other debris which cluttered the area for days.

And in the bay?

But all this was nothing to what went on in Lituya Bay. The people on the boats anchored there knew well what happened. Two of the boats were anchored just behind La Chaussee Spit. That tongue of land, piled high with rocks and covered by an evergreen thicket, protected them from the open sea. Bill Swanson and his wife were in the *Badger*.

In the *Sunmore* were Orville Wagner and his young bride Mickey. The third boat, the 38-foot *Edrie,* was anchored farther east in the bay near its south shore, with Howard Ulrich and his seven-year-old son aboard. All these people were jolted from their sleep. They jumped up in dazed unbelief to see a topsy-turvy world about them.

The Swansons watched in amazement as the mountains danced in the deepening evening light. They saw the beginnings of great landslides raising clouds of dust and snow. Then their attention centered on an unbelievable thing. The ice mass of Lituya Glacier, normally hidden far behind the north gateway peak, seemed to rise up in plain sight above the brow of the mountain, only to fall majestically into the water of the inner bay. It was like a nightmarish mirage!

The big wave came

Although six miles away, the commotion was awesome and frightening. The Swansons saw the water rise in a wave to engulf the headland of the north mountain. The wave then caromed down the bay, scouring the trees from the hillsides, destroying the recently vacated mountaineers' campsite, climbing in a watery mountain up the side of Cenotaph Island until it swallowed Huscroft's old cabin, and finally spilling in a deluge over the top of the island, a hundred and sixty-five feet above the bay.

The wave swirled Ulrich's boat out of control and came racing toward the Swanson and Wagner boats, still at anchor. To the horror of the people, it picked up the two craft, snapped their anchor chains, and carried them like surfboards in one of the wildest rides ever taken by any fishing boat. The Swansons said that they looked down on the tops of forty-foot trees and rocks as big as houses. They were swept completely over the spit into the sea!

The unfortunate Wagners were lost when their boat broke up, but the Swansons had the luck to be set down gently enough among the outer rocks to make their escape in a tiny punt. In it they drifted, dazed and exposed, until they were rescued. Later, after resting in a Juneau hospital, they described their fantastic experience.

Howard Ulrich and his boy Sonny also escaped by some miracle. Like the others, they were awakened by the hammering of the water against *Edrie's* hull. Ulrich heard a resounding crash from the head of the bay and watched the same soaring wave seen by the Swansons, but with a closer view. He watched in fascination as the ice of Lituya Glacier seemed to fall and dash the water far up the steep side of the north mountain — unbelievably high, he thought. He watched the wave start its march down the bay, sloshing along the hillsides and bouncing from side to side.

Suddenly Ulrich remembered he had to do something — and quickly! Desperately he started the engine so he could take up his anchor. But it was too slow. He could never make it. The wave, all of fifty feet high, overran Cenotaph Island. He thought of Sonny. He got a life jacket on him and cried out to hang on for dear life. Then he remembered his radio. Grabbing the mouthpiece he screamed the international distress call.

"Mayday! Mayday! *Edrie* in Lituya Bay! All Hell broken loose — I think we've had it. Goodbye!"

The ride

Ulrich watched the wave wash five hundred feet high on the south bank, then head for the *Edrie*. He tried to slip the anchor chain, but its inner end was tightly secured, and it wouldn't let go. He managed to head the boat toward the wave as she rode higher and ever higher. The chain tightened, then broke. The short end snapped up and wrapped around the pilot house.

Completely out of control, *Edrie* swooped high

over what had just been dry land. But she came back down on the backwash, whirling wildly in the churning water. The engine was still going, and Ulrich spent the next minutes maneuvering to escape the tumbling masses of ice, any one of which would have made kindling wood of the *Edrie*. Calling words of warning to Sonny to hang on for his very life, Ulrich gradually worked his way over the tossing bay toward the entrance.

It was the wrong time. The tide was running, and those sloshing waves would make the narrow channel all the more perilous. But Ulrich knew he had to run for it. Who knew what would happen next! He would never dare to stay in Lituya a moment longer than he had to. He tucked pillows about Sonny, and took the wheel to face what would probably be the most serious crisis of his life — and of Sonny's too!

Luck was with them. A fisherman friend had heard his frantic radio call, and appraised the situation. Taking station outside the channel, he showed a bright light for Ulrich to steer by in the late evening gloom. So the sturdy *Edrie* faced it. The current dashed her madly against the breakers and rips of the channel. They hit *Edrie* with brutal force. Three combers broke completely over her, and her timbers groaned in protest. She jumped and shook,

Courtesy Coast and Geodetic Survey

South shore of Lituya Bay, and the Fairweather Mountains, Alaska, after the great earthquake and wave of 1958, showing the scoured shore to heights of several hundreds of feet.

but she made it! The Ulrichs had ridden the highest wave ever known.

The highest wave of them all

How high was the wave in Lituya? And what caused it? Certainly it exceeded by far the heights of Miller's old trimlines. The naked hillsides down the length of the bay showed the heights it had reached — five hundred feet in places. The cause was not so easy to find. Photographs taken a few weeks later by a Coast and Geodetic Survey air photo mission were examined microscopically by experienced photo-interpreters of the Survey. It was clear that enormous masses of avalanche material had fallen into the bay from heights as great as three thousand feet on the bordering high mountains. Masses of ice had fallen from the towering face of Lituya Glacier, though this may have had little to do with generating the wave.

All this material dumped suddenly into the confined waters of the bay generated a wave possibly between fifty and a hundred feet high. This had such energy that it could slosh back and forth, rising on the hillsides according to their shapes. In the basin at Lituya's inner end the sloshing must have been very violent. The face of the north mountain showed bare rocks where dense forest had been — all the way to a height greater than seventeen hundred feet!

Was this a landslide? There was not a bit of landslide dirt or debris on the rocks! Observers in small planes — even geologists Miller and Mann in helicopters — marveled at how clean the rock had been washed. The photo-interpreters at Washing-

Scour on the brow of the north mountain, Lituya Bay, Alaska, after the great earthquake and wave of 1958. The water rose more than 1700 feet up the mountainside to tear away the forest and every bit of soil from the rocks!

ton agreed. Professor Wiegel of the University of California demonstrated in a model experiment that the wave height found by these people was perfectly possible. Still, there were doubters. Who ever heard of such a wave?

Perhaps the best evidence of all was the discovery, by Dr. Miller himself, of trees at the top of the bared area, a little more than seventeen hundred feet above the bay, bent and broken with their trunks lying uphill from their roots. The roots had not been torn from the ground — something had pushed the trees up. The great force to do this could have been nothing but the topmost waters of the giant wave that swept the mountain that evening in 1958.

That wave had the height of ten Niagaras! Scientists no longer doubt the meaning of Don Miller's trimlines.

XI

Making the Best of Earthquakes

Nature is not governed except by obeying her.
— BACON

L. Don Leet has remarked that man is his own worst enemy, at least as far as earthquakes are concerned. Somehow it seems easy to apply Leet's criticism to many of man's dealings with life on this planet. But those are not the subject of this book — back to earthquakes!

Man's own structures trap him when the earth quakes. By far most human deaths in earthquakes and their associated fires, floods, and other effects, are due to falling buildings.

What can be done about this?

It should be obvious that we cannot stop earthquakes. Even stronger beings than the Roman gods will never have that power. So we have to put up

with them — to accept them and make the best prep-
arations for them that we can.

It is almost as obvious that man cannot predict
them — not yet at any rate. Even if he could it
might save some lives but by no means all. The
example of the tsunami warnings at Hilo has given
proof of this. As for property, we wouldn't be able
to save any of it to speak of, simply by warnings.

So it appears that man has to learn how to build
houses and buildings — dams, bridges, and all the
rest — so earthquakes will not destroy them. This
isn't easy, but much careful work has been done
on the problem, and it will be solved completely
in time.

Danger from above

The only earthquake death in the history of England, where such shocks are rare and at worst slight,
was in 1580, when an apprentice was killed by a
stone falling from a building. This seemingly unim-
portant loss points out a major precaution. One
mustn't encumber houses in earthquake zones with
things that can fall upon people. Thousands have
been killed by debris from flimsy parapet walls
around the roofs, by falling roof tiles, and by other
material that smashes down upon the sidewalks. Of
all these, falling chimneys are by far the greatest

A new high school destroyed by the Helena, Montana, earthquake of 1935. Engineers who design buildings in earthquake areas hope in future to avoid such dangers.

single danger, at least in communities of wood frame houses. Eiby says that twenty thousand chimneys near Wellington needed repairs after the 1942 earthquakes in New Zealand.

We have learned some of these things by experience. Building codes in many earthquake areas now have much to say about the ornamental trifles with which architects formerly liked to adorn buildings, but which can fall off all too easily. Times are changing, and there may be a day when all big city buildings will be free of gargoyles, carved stonework, "gingerbread" and the other unsightly gimcrackery once so highly regarded in our city culture. Getting rid of it ought to be simply a matter of artistic taste, but perhaps the help of earthquakes is necessary. It seems to me that if earthquakes can achieve that kind of cleanup, they can't be all bad.

The horrors of the earthquake fires at Lisbon, San Francisco, and Tokyo have shown how vital it is to maintain disaster-proof fire-fighting facilities. Above all this means infallible water supplies. Much engineering ingenuity has been exercised to achieve this protection in many places.

Danger from below

Another thing we can do is to place our buildings away from active earthquake faults. Unfortunately, this is not always done. Perhaps small houses are not quite so much in danger — Professor Byerly lives in a house almost over one of California's very bad faults. It may be a good gamble. Perhaps it will be long before an earthquake visits that fault. Perhaps too, like the shack next to the great Nevada fault, there wouldn't be much damage anyway. The house at the end of the walkway broken by the San Andreas faulting in 1906 wasn't badly hurt either.

But we must be careful of faults. The town of Anjar in the Rann of Cutch in Indiá lay over the fault that broke in such violent scarp motion in 1819. After the earthquake, half the town survived on the uplifted side of the fault; the other half had subsided into a watery morass on the sunken side. Three thousand houses were ruined. When Anjar was built there was probably no one who knew the fault existed.

In particular, we must safeguard dams that might break to release disastrous floods, or bridges that could fall with people on them. It is easy to imagine what would happen to the Grand Coulee dam or to the Golden Gate bridge if the distances between their abutments were to change several feet. Such a change destroyed the Southern Pacific Railway tracks in the Tehachapi Mountains. Unfortunately our railways, if they are to reach anywhere, have to cross the entire countryside. But we cannot have other important structures lying across earthquake faults. We must therefore plan our building projects with the help of geological studies and advice about faults.

Wherever one is, the shaking of the ground has to be contended with. This may be severe, even far from a fault. It was reported after the Assam earthquake of 1897 that the surface of the ground had vibrated in every direction so it looked like a storm-tossed sea. It was as if it had been plowed. The turf was torn, and sods were scattered in every direction.

It is necessary therefore to build strongly enough so our buildings will stand safely even when they are shaken violently. They must be flexible, too.

Giving with the punch

Enormous losses of people have resulted from the collapse of mud huts and stone houses. Historically these have been built with no regard for any force but the steady pull of gravity to hold them together. The enormous housing projects near Moscow and other large Russian cities are Soviet attempts to cope with rocketing population figures. They wish to get the most housing with the least cost in work, materials, and time, which they prefer to save for their industry and armaments. The Russian apartment houses are built therefore without framework. There is nothing but gravity to hold together the parts of large buildings that will house hundreds of people. It is appalling to think of the tragic results of a possible strong earthquake at Moscow. Fortunately for the Muscovites, there is no reason to expect one — but as we have seen, it could happen!

Turkey is an area of greater danger. Constantinople was so shaken during the entire year 740 A.D. that the emperor and nearly the entire population left their houses in fear of collapse. They saved themselves in the only way they knew — by dwell-

ing in tents in the fields. That is somewhat incon-
venient. It would have been far more comfortable
to have made their buildings safe to live in, in the
first place. But they didn't know how! It is not easy,
but it is the world's principal problem in connection
with saving lives during earthquakes.

Some very interesting new ideas in building have
been tried. The famous architect Frank Lloyd
Wright designed the Imperial Hotel in Tokyo as a
low, rambling structure of very flexible wood construction. He also specified a flat, mattress-like foundation, almost literally floating like a boat in the soft
earth of Tokyo. This was intended to allow the
building to ride loosely on the shaking earth —
which would never be possible if there were long
pilings reaching down into the harder layers below.
As if to prove that Architect Wright knew well what
he was doing, the hotel went through the 1923 catastrophe with but slight damage.

An imaginative engineer designed a new upper
story for a large retail store in Los Angeles, with
the new part resting on rollers. If the building were
shaken the upper part would ride free, in the manner
of the Imperial Hotel. There has been no effective
test of this novel idea, but it looks like something
that would work!

Other engineers have suggested putting strong

springs into the bracing of elevated water tanks, to absorb the stresses and prevent breaking of the tie rods. It is particularly important, as we have seen, to save water tanks from collapse, because of the need of water for fighting fires.

The engineer takes a look

It is not yet known whether modern buildings are designed as efficiently as possible. Perhaps they are even unnecessarily strong. Because of the great investment in buildings in our country it is important to know this, too. Seismologists and engineers have long been interested in the scientific study of earthquake effects in buildings, in order to learn the most effective and economical way of countering the stresses induced by shaking.

After the Lisbon tragedy the Marques de Pombal, the strong administrator who restored the city to a continuing life, sent inquiries to every parish in the country. Questions were asked about the effects felt by the people — the time of the shock; its duration; the effects on the sea, springs, and rivers; the ground fissures; and the details of houses collapsed or burned. Meanwhile a Japanese engineer studied the effects in a diligent search for useful lessons for his own people at home. These efforts may be looked on as the beginning of modern *engineering seismol-*

ogy — the science of building structures on engineering principles to be safe from earthquake failure.

The Neapolitan Academy of Sciences and Fine Letters appointed the first serious scientific commission in history to investigate the effects of a great earthquake — that at Calabria, Italy, in 1783. This, though a step in the right direction, was doomed to insignificant results because of the essential lack of technical engineering knowledge in those days.

Even more serious efforts followed the Italian earthquakes of 1857. The Irish engineer Mallet made excellent studies resulting in some general principles for human protection which we still honor today. Among his works were two volumes in 1862 on *The Great Neapolitan Earthquake of 1857: the First Principles of Observational Seismology.* He also presented maps showing, in four zones, where towns were destroyed, where large buildings collapsed and men died, where there was minor damage, and where the shock was felt but no damage resulted. This kind of study is made even today after strong American shocks.

Engineering seismology entered its present phase of development in America in the 1920's. Too many buildings were suffering in the shocks of the western states. In 1929 a number of American engineers attended an international meeting in Japan, where they were impressed with the high Japanese interest in reducing earthquake losses. They returned with great determination to start truly scientific studies of the problem.

They take its measure

It was by now correctly supposed that the first task was to measure the ground motions to see what engineers had to contend with. This wasn't simple, for the motion is highly irregular — chaotic, in fact. Every earthquake produces a long series of shifty ground motions, and no two earthquakes are alike.

What seemed to be the most significant things about the motion were the *amplitude,* or size of back-and-forth motion, and the *acceleration,* or changing rate of the motion. The acceleration is what jerks things. Rough measurements were made by setting rods of different lengths on end in a row to see which ones fell over when the ground shook. This could give only very rough ideas about the strength of the motion. It was not good enough. Instruments were needed.

The Coast and Geodetic Survey, which already had responsibility for national earthquake studies, entered vigorously into the work. Survey men developed new instruments known as *strong-motion* seismographs. Unlike usual seismographs, which

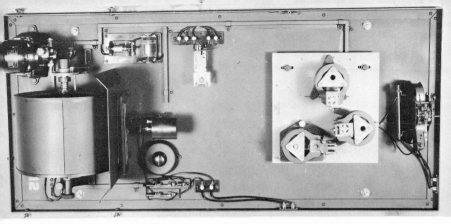

Top view of a strong-motion seismograph used to determine the character of the ground motions that knock down buildings in strong earthquakes. The three sensitive units at the right detect and measure the motions in the east-west, north-south, and up-down directions, sending their messages on beams of light to a photographic record paper wound around the turning drum at the left. The records help engineers design safe buildings.

are highly sensitive so as to detect very distant shocks, these are less sensitive, and designed to make correct recordings of the strong ground motions near the centers of damaging shocks. The characteristics of the ground motion are measured very accurately, which pleases engineers planning to use those measurements in their mathematical work.

The Survey men are still at work in California. They study the effects of strong shocks in their area and prepare engineering reports of building damage. They send out questionnaires much as Pombal did two centuries ago, and make maps of damage areas as Mallet did a century later.

Shaking machines have been developed, with un-
evenly weighted flywheels run by electric motors at
different speeds while clamped to the frames of
buildings. Shaken mildly in this way the buildings
demonstrate their natural vibration tendencies. Vibration meters record the shaking speeds which most
affect the buildings. This is important, for the tendency of a building to vibrate most easily at certain
frequencies governs how it will react to earthquake
motions. Engineers learn from such tests. Their
ability to design suitable natural frequencies for a
building is their principal way of avoiding a dangerous structure.

After the Survey program was started, with a number of the new instruments installed in California
locations, there began a long wait for damaging
earthquakes. It was like fishing where the nibbles
were far between. Earthquakes came, but usually in
places far from the instruments. The forty-one-mil-
lion-dollar Long Beach earthquake of 1933 was the
first important one to produce important records.
That earthquake, incidentally, spurred the program
vigorously, for many school buildings were destroyed, and the people of California realized with
horror that, had the shock been a few hours earlier,
many children would have been added to the already
tragic toll of 120 dead.

Since then more instruments have been installed, and there have been good records of several strong shocks. To speed the collection of data about ground motions, strong-motion seismographs have been installed in many places — even in parts of South America. Our Latin American friends operate them and send records to the Survey men in California after they have had earthquakes.

The study of the records goes on in Japan, South America, and other parts of the world, as well as at home. Great electronic computers have been put to work trying to make mathematical sense out of the complex variety of strong ground motions put on record by the instruments. In spite of all this, important new engineering information has been slow in coming. The really technical problem is not yet completely solved.

Safe enough?

Meanwhile engineers have learned enough in a general way about building methods to believe that most modern steel frame buildings are reasonably safe, particularly when on solid land. Tall steel buildings are resilient as well as strong, and usually present no greater hazard than the fall of loose fixtures or goods from store shelves.

Wood frame houses are also very flexible and little

likely to collapse, even in very strong shocks. Many in fact withstood the San Francisco shock, only to fall prey to the fire! People in them are in no great danger unless they have the poor luck to be in the way of the mantel clock, or loose ceiling plaster, or bricks fallen through the roof from the chimney.

What you can do

Seismologists are asked with great regularity what people should do about earthquakes. Answering that question is not too difficult, for there are a few practical rules of undoubted value. House dwellers should be sure the chimney is sound and strong, and no taller than it has to be. Emergency cooking fires in fireplaces should never be lit after an earthquake. Many house fires have been started that way, because the brickwork has developed cracks through which the heat can go into the wood frame. Then is the worst possible time to have a house fire, for the water service may be stopped, and fire engines may not be able to get through the littered streets.

Most people say that during the earthquake one should not run to the street. It may be more dangerous, on account of falling objects, than inside. The safest places are under doorways or other reinforced places away from falling plaster. Many prefer to crawl under strong tables or desks where the rubble may not fall on their heads. In any event, the chances are it will all be over in a very short time. Dr. Bailey Willis, the great California geologist of revered memory, has said, "Stand still and count to forty. Then it makes no difference what you do."

It has been reported that many Japanese believe it best to run out into a bamboo thicket, where the tangle of roots cushions the shock. This advice wouldn't help much in America, even if it were true — which it isn't. Many Japanese are somewhat hardened to the idea of earthquakes, though they all do in truth worry about them. Most stay where they are on the theory that it'll be over soon. Some even pretend they don't notice, being too busy with their reading or whatever they are doing. But they do notice. Any one of the thousands of shocks felt in Japan every year may be the next big one.

Nothing much has been said on the *good* side about earthquakes. To tell the truth, there isn't much good to *be* said of them, except that cities devastated by earthquakes and resulting fires have to be rebuilt. This may be more a blessing in many cases than one might think offhand. It was a blessing at Port Royal.

Earthquake disasters have in fact often been the means ordained by Nature for getting rid of sordid slums, and for rebuilding with good civic plans, and modern, sanitary, efficient, and *earthquake-resistant* buildings. It is strange that Nature should have to make man do what he ought to do anyway. Man is indeed his own worst enemy in some things — especially in matters of our quaking earth!

Recommended Reading

EIBY, G. A., *About Earthquakes,* Harper & Brothers, 1957.

HECK, NICHOLAS HUNTER, *Earthquakes,* Princeton University Press, 1936.

LEET, L. DON, *Causes of Catastrophe,* Whittlesey House, McGraw-Hill Book Company, 1948.

MACELWANE, JAMES B., *When the Earth Quakes,* The Bruce Publishing Company, 1947.

Glossary of Terms

Aftershock. Lesser earthquake following main shock.
Amplitude. Length of back-and-forth motions.

Bedrock. Solid layers of rock.
Bore. Tide-induced wave in an estuary or bay.

Compensation, isostatic. Balancing of pressure inside earth.
Crust. Outer layers of earth rocks.

Deep-focus earthquake. Unusually deep earthquake.

Earthquake. Breaking of rock strata.
Elastic rebound theory. Theory that earthquakes depend on rock elasticity.
Engineering seismology. Application of earthquake studies to engineering, and development of earthquake-resistant construction methods.

235

Epicenter. Point on earth's surface directly above an earthquake focus.

Erg. Small unit of energy.

Escarpment. Mountain wall caused by elevation of a block of land.

Fault. Break in earth rocks due to earthquake.

Focus. Origin of earthquake reaction.

Foreshock. Smaller earthquake preceding main shock.

Galvanometer. Electric current detector.

Geologist. Scientist concerned with the earth and its rocks.

Geophone. Detector of earth vibrations.

Inertia. Inherent resistance to applied force.

Intensity scale. Scale for rating earthquakes according to effects.

Isoseismal; isoseismic. Having equal violence of earthquake effects.

Isoseismal map. Map of equal-intensity (isoseismal) lines.

Loess. Deep deposit of airborne dust.

Love wave. Transverse wave first described by Love.

L-wave. Long, slow earthquake wave.

Magnitude scale. Scale for rating earthquake energy.

Mantle. Layer of earth lying outside the core and under the crust.

Microseism. Small earth tremor.

Modified Mercalli Scale. Scale for rating earthquakes according to effects.

Moho. Boundary between earth crust and mantle, discovered by Mohorovičić.

Mohole. Proposed drill hole through earth crust.

Oceanographer. Ocean scientist.

Pendulum. Body suspended from fixed point so as to hang or swing freely.

P-wave. Primary or pressure type of earthquake wave.

Radioactivity. Atomic reaction.

Rayleigh wave. Earth motion characterized by elliptical particle motions.

Richter Scale. Magnitude scale in common use for rating earthquake energy.

Rockburst. Breaking of stressed rocks in mines.

Roots, mountain. Deeper crustal layers under mountains.

Rossi-Forel Scale. Rating scale for earthquakes according to effects.

Scarp. Steep side of an uplifted earth area.

Seiche. Oscillation of water in a bay.

Seism. Earthquake (from Greek *seismos,* earthquake).

Seismal; seismic. Pertaining to earthquakes.

Seismic prospecting. Search for oil or minerals, using explosion-induced earth waves.

Seismic sea wave. Ocean wave disturbance related to an undersea earthquake.

Seismogram. Earthquake wave record.

Seismograph. Recording and timing seismometer.

Seismologist. Earthquake scientist.

Seismology. Science of earthquake study.

Seismometer. Detector of earthquake waves.

Seismoscope. Earthquake indicator without timing.

Shear. Force resulting in side-to-side motion.

S-wave. Secondary or shear type of earthquake wave.

Tectonic. Relating to earth structure.

Tsunami. Seismic sea wave.

Index

239